IN THE
DARK

JASON BAWDEN-SMITH

JASON BAWDEN-SMITH

IN THE
DARK

NEW WAYS TO AVOID
THE HARMFUL EFFECTS OF LIVING IN A
TECHNOLOGICALLY CONNECTED WORLD

First published November 2016 by Major Street Publishing Pty Ltd
Contact: E info@majorstreet.com.au | M 0421 707 983
Revised edition published April 2017

National Library of Australia Cataloguing-in-Publication entry
Title: In the dark: new ways to avoid the harmful effects of living in a technologically
connected world/Jason Bawden-Smith.
ISBN: 9780994542465 (paperback)
Subjects: Electromagnetic ground waves – Health aspects.
Blue light – Health aspects. Technology – Health aspects.
Dewey Number: 612.01442

Internal design by Production Works
Printed in Australia by McPhersons Printing

10 9 8 7 6 5 4 3 2 1

ISBN: 978-0-9945424-6-5

Dedication

For all sufferers of modern disease, fighting the good fight to regain their right to thrive – this book is for you. We must appreciate and acknowledge our relationship with nature and re-establish our connection with Mother Earth and Father Sun to regain optimal health. Only when we understand how technology and indoor living is impacting our biology can we advance as a modern civilisation to experience lasting longevity and true wealth.

Contents

PART 4: SHADOWS IN THE FUTURE

My complaint is my call to action

IF I went back in time to tell the younger version of myself, 'Jason, you're going to bust some of the biggest environmental cover-ups in Australia, build a multimillion-dollar environmental consulting company and write multiple books about your experiences', I would have laughed and responded, 'Yeah, right!'

Yes, right, indeed.

Sometimes in life, we are presented with information that can impact the lives of millions of people worldwide. When it lands in our hands, we have to make a choice: to do it justice with all our heart, or to walk away and pretend it never presented itself. Typically, I take the first option.

The first major problem I came across was the beach pollution in Sydney.

'Damn surf is disgusting'

It was 1982, and a sunny, clear and moderately warm day. I was 16 years old and listening to the song 'One Perfect Day' by The Little Heroes before hitting the surf at Maroubra beach. There were four-foot sets coming through, offshore winds and the sand banks were perfect – it was any surfer's dream. But as I paddled out to the breaks, I looked around and saw condoms, toilet paper, tampons and a whole lot of human faeces floating in the water. So much for the romance of the day! It was a killjoy and an environmental outrage.

When I got home, it took me a good 30 minutes of bathing and almost a whole bar of soap to wash off the stench. But that wasn't the worst of it. My ear got infected, and that has put my balance off for most of my life.

'Damn surf is disgusting!' I complained to my mother, Judith. She replied, 'Well, you're going to have to do something about it!' Judith wasn't one for indulging me in my drama or my complaining. Her approach could be summed up as, 'Your complaint is your call to action' – which is now my motto.

Over the next six years, I started a small campaign group and went from being a teenage 'delinquent' to attaining a Bachelor of Applied Science in Environmental Health with a Major in Water Quality. (During my time in academia, I published a total of eleven peer-reviewed scientific papers, including three in the *Medical Journal of Australia*.) I then joined the New South Wales Department of Health's environmental health division, focusing on water quality, and I got involved in a study that later became the Beachwatch Program.

In the end, I leaked the Department of Health's water pollution statistics to the media, which forced the government to fix the issue. As a result, the sewerage treatment plants were upgraded and the ocean outfall extended to 1.7 km out to sea, where the continental shelf drops out. I'm proud to say that today, the eastern beaches in Sydney are among the finest and cleanest in the world. The whales have come back; they even came to visit me there once, almost as if to say, 'Well done, mate'.

Poisonous paint

The next problem that found me was lead in paint. It was killing dogs and poisoning children, and it was in housing built up until the 1970s. The older the house, the more lead paint there was on its surfaces.

I was in the process of getting my Master's degree in Environmental Science and was looking for a major project that would dovetail with my work at NSW Health. One day, a new community paediatrician named Garth walked into our office. He had spent years working in American ghettos and had a particular interest in lead poisoning in children. 'What are you doing about environmental lead?' he asked us.

After some research, it became clear that lead might indeed be a problem in Sydney. My proposal for a Mort Bay, Balmain study of environmental lead was accepted by the university, and I began to measure the levels of lead in soil, paint, dust and blood in that area. What I found was shocking. Over half of the children in the study area had blood lead levels over the safe recommended level, and the levels of lead in soil, dust and paint were almost as high as those found near lead smelters and mines.

I handed in my thesis on a Friday. On Monday, I was called by a reporter. I later discovered that one of the environmental science lecturers at the university had helped to release my report to the media after testing his own children and finding they had elevated blood lead levels.

At the time, industry and government were pinning the lead-poisoning problem on the lead in petrol. Lead petrol had to be phased out anyway, as it damaged the catalytic converters being introduced to reduce air pollution.

All too often, government and industry make a mistake and pin a problem on the wrong source, and the repercussions can be serious. It's not industry's fault, in my opinion. It's the fact that the majority of key influencers haven't been educated on the importance of taking into account the potential long-term health effects of economic decisions. Rather than looking at factors in isolation, they need to take a more holistic and integrated approach.

Now, property values are a sacred cow in Australia. You can imagine the cost of the remedial work and the potential impact on property values if lead paint was found to be responsible for the poisoning. Removing lead paint from houses is a far more intractable and complex task than removing lead from petrol! I hoped that I was wrong and that lead paint wasn't the primary culprit – but my published research made it clear that it was.

The truth came out nationwide in March 1992 on ABC TV's flagship current affairs program at the time, *The 7.30 Report*.

Difficult as such problems may be to fix, the community has more compassion for people who illuminate them early than it does for those who try to cover them up and have them revealed later by some 'accidental leak.'

Environmental science and entrepreneurialism

It's my belief that environmental science is meant to be socially just, not just economically viable. Science should be used to serve the people, not just create a fat balance sheet.

I'm certain that tackling problems head on, rather than trying to deny them, is much more profitable for businesses long term. But to do that requires courage to stand up for humanity, rather than focusing on a bank balance. It requires rigorous efforts to educate the community. It requires critical thinking. It requires you to pass on what you know in a way that the everyday person can understand – not just the elite privileged few who make decisions on our behalf. When everyone is privileged, then humanity can prosper.

I'm not a Luddite – I love technology and have been addicted to it since *Tennis for Two* was around. (A game played on an oscillosope, like the monitors you may have seen in hospitals that track patients' heartbeats.) I built my business fortune on the technology I used to address environmental problems. In the course of my research into the lead paint problem, I invested in state-of-the-art, hand-held, X-ray fluorescence spectrum analysers that tested for lead in and around homes, parks and factories in Australia. These devices helped to identify contamination and coordinate cost-effective remediation programs. Not only were we able to help minimise the risk of lead-poisoning for hundreds of children, but it provided us with a marketing advantage to build one of the largest and most successful contaminated-land consultancy companies in Australia, JBS&G, with over 100 employees and offices around Australia.

In the late 1990s, I introduced this technology into the mining industry – something that was considered an 'impossible application' by the manufacturer. Such instruments are now found on exploration and mining sites around the world.

With precise, on-the-spot data on the metal content of soil, sediment and ore that the portable X-ray analysers provide, geologists and engineers can better target mineralisation, reduce the damage to the local environment and minimise the impact of mining on the earth. Simply put, the results are less waste and less mess. Dollars are saved and the environmental impact is minimised simultaneously with the use of technology.

I eventually sold the technology business for $5.5 million in 2008. If you're interested, you can read more about my life as an environmental entrepreneur in my first book, *Making Waves*.

Used correctly, with due consideration to the environment, technology can be life-enhancing. It can provide solutions to serious problems, resources to a rapidly populating planet and entertainment. There's no argument about that. However, often we only discover a technology's adverse repercussions long after it has spread into our daily lives.

The dark side of modern technology

In the Dark is where my journey continues – where I received my next call to action. I started becoming interested in the connection between physics and biology at the end of 2015. 'Why don't we talk about them in the same sentence?' I asked myself. 'We regularly connect biology and chemistry (biochemistry) in nutrition and exercise.' I wondered what role physics and the environment played in human health. Shortly afterward, I heard an interview with Dr Jack Kruse, a respected neurosurgeon and pioneer of quantum biology, and had the first of many 'Aha!' moments.

As I began to connect the dots between physics and health, and in particular to study the impact of light and harmful electromagnetic frequencies (EMFs) on human biology, I realised that I had found an explanation – not only for my own health problems at the time, but also for my mother's much more serious illness.

My mother passed away a few years ago, but she was ill for most of her life. Experiencing lethargy and excruciating pain, my mother was frequently bedridden and very sensitive to various chemicals and EMFs. Most health professionals diagnosed her with a severe form of Chronic Fatigue Syndrome (Myalgic Encephalomyelitis), a complex illness the cause of which is still unknown and for which there was no cure. My mother and I were very close, and searching for a cause and effective treatment for her became an obsession for me.

I invested decades of my life and hundreds of thousands of dollars, consulting everyone from Australia's top medical specialists to faith healers and shamans, but with no success. My mother moved out of the city to a pristine mountain location to try to limit the impact of EMFs and chemicals, but we could never figure out what was causing her illness and so we couldn't find a solution for her. If only I had known then what I know now! I believe what was making her sick was her indoor lifestyle, being constantly bathed in artificial light and rarely having any contact with sunlight or the earth.

My personal health issues at the end of 2015 seem to have had the same cause. My blood tests showed high insulin levels and high cholesterol, I had a history of high blood pressure and I was overweight. I was pre-diabetic, and my doctor's diagnosis was metabolic syndrome. He wanted to take me down the typical medical path of exercise and healthy eating, and then, if necessary, blood-glucose-reducing medication.

But my research was indicating that light and EMFs might be bigger culprits – things that even the best doctors were still in the dark about. For the previous 20 years, I had worked as a managing director in an artificially lit office, bathed in wi-fi signals and surrounded by communication towers, getting to work early and leaving after sunset. I never saw the sun during the week – and worse yet, when I got home I would stare at a computer screen or watch TV. That's about 16 hours of exposure to blue light every day, and no sunlight except during my weekend trip to the beach. To cap it off, whenever I did get out into the sun, I wore sunglasses and sunscreen!

So, I began using the strategies I describe in Part 3 of this book, and less than a year later my symptoms have dramatically improved. I have even gone down three notches on my belt by changing the time of day I eat, minimising blue light exposure at night and getting morning sun. I am convinced I had what I have begun calling 'blue light disease' – a pre-diabetic state caused by excessive exposure to artificial blue light and harmful EMFs.

Based on my research, I believe that our immersion in artificial light and harmful electromagnetic fields constitutes one of the biggest threats to humanity's health, freedom and prosperity. They're the dark side of technology. This is what I discuss in this book.

About the book

I have divided *In the Dark* into four parts:

- **Part 1: In the light** aims to give you a solid understanding of how light affects human health and the implications of artificial light for our well-being.
- **Part 2: Electri-fried** looks at the different types of EMFs and how some – what I call 'manmade EMFs' – can have a negative impact on human health.
- **Part 3: What you can do** examines the practical ways you can protect yourself and your loved ones – including the emerging technological solutions available.

- **Part 4: Shadows in the future** briefly looks at what the future may hold and encourages budding entrepreneurs to become part of the solution.

You will find that there's still some controversy in mainstream media and medicine about EMFs in particular, so I have dedicated a chapter in Part 2 to discussing this. I have also provided references at the end of the book so you can do your own research. And why not do your own personal trial of the mitigation strategies in Part 3? You may well rid yourself of niggly health conditions that haven't responded to any other therapies or treatments!

I believe humanity is facing a significant challenge, but one that we're more than capable of addressing. We must search for a deep understanding of the problems, looking through the lens of a physicist, to minimise the effects those problems have on us as best we can and use innovation and bold entrepreneurship to create better solutions for the future.

My intention for this book is to share all that I have learned, so that you and your loved ones are empowered to take action to help yourselves thrive. Let's get into it!

PART ONE

IN THE LIGHT

'All life originates and develops under
the influence of … light …'

—*Goethe*

ONE

Light and health

'Food is simply sunlight in cold storage.'

—*John Harvey Kellogg*

L ET me take you somewhere scenic – by the ocean, on some tropical island. It's a place to recharge, to find a greater sense of peace and physical well-being. Now, picture a man looking at the horizon from his balcony, surrounded by trees, ocean and wildlife. He has a comfortable home with stunning views. He gets to wake up when the sun rises, swim, eat well, have massages, be entertained with music and go to sleep when the sun sets. There's nothing he *has* to do, no deadlines, no one to bug him, no smartphones, no waiting in long queues.

Basically, he lives in a world devoid of the hassles of a modern lifestyle, far away from traffic jams, noisy neighbours, eating lunch in front of a computer screen and falling asleep at a desk at midnight.

Take a closer look at our imaginary protagonist. Look at his muscle tone, posture, skin and hair – he radiates vitality. He has a clean, healthy lifestyle, with no binge-eating, excessive alcohol consumption or other addictions. His skin is supple and his hair is thick. It's hard to imagine he's any older than 30, but he is: he's close to 50. One thing's for sure, he's doing something right!

So what's his secret? He gets regular exercise swimming in the ocean, maybe it's that? Or is it that he eats a well-balanced diet consisting of greens, seafood, lean proteins and limited processed food? Some people may suggest that he's taking some of those supplements that promise superhuman health benefits!

What if it were a lot simpler than that, though? Sure, healthy habits, exercise and a good diet contribute to better health, but what if the path to longevity were governed by more fundamental principles? Simple principles that tell you to reconnect with nature by exposing your eyes and skin to the morning sun, bathing your body in the ocean, and walking barefoot on the sand and grass? It's how human beings lived for centuries, after all.

As you will discover, there is compelling scientific evidence that humans should embrace this traditional way of living and more closely align with their natural world.

The power of light

The first secret to better health lies in the human eye, as John N. Ott[1] identified in the 1970s. Let's focus again on the man looking at the horizon, absorbing the full spectrum of morning sunlight from the sunrise, without filters or sunglasses. The light enters his eyes, hits his retinas and is converted to electrical signals in his brain which then travel through every system of his body, promoting healthy function (the Appendix goes into more detail about how this works).

Meanwhile, the sunlight (in particular the ultraviolet spectrum, which I'll clarify more soon) hits the man's skin and docosahexaenoic acid (DHA), an omega-3 fatty acid, allows his body to turn light into electricity. DHA is the only naturally occurring compound we know at this time that can turn UV light into DC electric current.[2]

The higher the current, the more energy we have. The lower it is, the more health problems we have. It's claimed by some scientists that many autoimmune diseases are caused by insufficient levels of light being stored within the nuclei of our cells.[3]

Think about it another way. The modern home needs electricity to function. Electrical circuits and wires in the house power its lighting, heating, security and connectivity. When the electrical signal is a stable voltage, most appliances in a modern home will function nicely. You have power and light on demand, so that you can watch TV, cook, have a hot shower and work under lights into the night.

The same thing happens with your body. Full-spectrum natural light supports your bodily functions, being converted into electrical signals (electrons) for use throughout the body. With the right signals, your body functions in an optimum state. You are literally generating electricity by digesting light with your eyes and ingesting light with your skin![4]

Who would figure that so much is going on? We thought we were just imagining some guy staring at a sunrise! Think about this, let it sink in. Look around you – all that you see is visible because of light. And all the light that is entering your eyes and in contact with your skin is directly affecting the way your body's processes are being regulated.

So there you are, sitting and reading this book, with full

spectrum sunlight responsible for your breathing, muscle tension, mental clarity, hunger levels – even your emotions. Have you seen the light?

What is full-spectrum light?

Visible light is one tiny band of the electromagnetic spectrum. As you can see in this diagram, the spectrum extends from low frequencies, often used in radio communication (on the right) to gamma and cosmic radiation with a short wavelength but high frequency (on the left). There are wavelengths as large as thousands of kilometres, and ones as small as 400 to 700 nanometres – and they all affect us.

Figure 1.1: The visible light spectrum

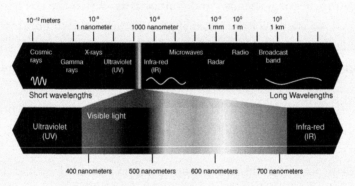

'Full-spectrum' light is light in the electromagnetic spectrum between infra-red and near-ultraviolet, and includes the visible spectrum of light (what we can see). Sunlight is considered full-spectrum light, even though the distribution of light that reaches earth changes with the time of day, latitude and atmospheric conditions. Full-spectrum light is what's needed to keep the body's intricate mechanics and internal clock in sync with the natural environment – it's critical for well-being. You can get sunlight through glass windows, but the glass filters out essential UV parts of the natural light spectrum.

What trees and humans have in common

Here's a question for you: 'What does a tree and a human being have in common?' The answer is, 'More than you think'. Understanding this is going to be important as we delve more into how and why technology has harmful effects on your body.

Trees and human beings work together in a perfectly coupled system. I'm sure you remember your basic science lessons. A tree takes in carbon dioxide and sunlight, and expels oxygen during the day. Human beings do the opposite: we inhale oxygen and exhale carbon dioxide.

If a tree doesn't get enough natural light, its growth will be stunted; and if you cover a tree with a tarp it will die fairly quickly.[5] Similarly, if you keep a human in the dark for too long, their health will decay.

At the other end of the scale, a tree will also suffer if it is constantly bombarded with light with no chance to rest. Few trees grow in the regions at the 59th parallel – a circle 59 degrees north of the equator that crosses the northern tips of Scotland, Norway, Russia and Alaska – where the sun is visible for more than 18 hours a day in summer. Similarly, if you keep bombarding a human being with artificial lighting, without ever giving them a chance to rest in the dark, you'll drive them nuts and their health will decay too.

There is a primary difference between how humans and trees replenish their energy. Trees are permanently connected to the earth via their deep root system and 100 per cent connected to the sun through its canopy (branches and leaves). This direct and permanent connection to the earth and sun means the tree can grow and survive without having to eat. Humans are not permanently connected to nature so we have to roam the earth to find food and eat it – though these days, usually we 'hunt' in an artificially lit supermarket or restaurant.

To put it another way, when humans burn energy, we lose electrons. There are three main ways to replace these electrons, two of which are similar to how trees operate:

1. 'Drinking' in the sun's rays (light energy, or photons) through our eyes and skin
2. Walking barefoot on the beach or in the park and absorbing negatively-charged electrons through grounding or earthing – coupling your body to the earth's surface energy through direct contact with it[6]
3. Consuming food.

'Mighty-chondria' and heteroplasmy – charging your batteries

I call mitochondria, 'mighty-chondria', and there's a reason for that. Think of the mitochondria as an energy factory or battery plant for your cells. Each mitochondrion contains its own DNA, separate to the commonly known nuclear DNA genome, called 'mitochondrial DNA', which encodes the wiring diagram for the cell's power plants. This is nerdy I know, but bear with me.

So what is so 'mighty' about mitochondria? Well, first of all, we inherit our mitochondrial DNA solely from our mother – and a woman's mitochondrial DNA make-up from the environment in which she lives is imprinted in her mitochondrial DNA and passed on to her children. So for example, if your grandmother was born in Singapore and you live in London, you're in a different environment to that for which your mitochondrial DNA was developed. It's important to know the environment in which your grandmother and your mother were born if you're trying to achieve optimal health. How your body is built to live in this world largely depends on your mitochondria DNA, not the genes or DNA in your cell nucleus.

As Douglas Wallace[7], a geneticist and evolutionary biologist from the University of Pennsylvania will tell you, mitochondrial DNA and something called 'percent heteroplasmy' determine how well-charged your mitochondria batteries are. Percent heteroplasmy refers to how many mitochondria within a cell have mutant DNA.

When the proportion of mutant mitochondria in a cell goes above a certain threshold, the cell expresses dysfunction and eventually disease. Wallace found that alterations in mitochondrial DNA measured by levels of percentage of mutant mitochondrial DNA (called heteroplasmy), can account for 85 per cent of metabolic and degenerative diseases, including cancer.[8]

Figure 1.2: Normal healthy and mutant mitochondria

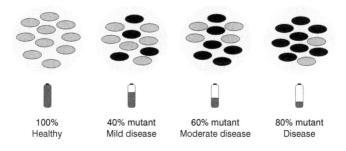

| 100% | 40% mutant | 60% mutant | 80% mutant |
| Healthy | Mild disease | Moderate disease | Disease |

So, the higher the heteroplasmy, the worse the cell's 'battery condition' is. The lower the heteroplasmy, the better the battery condition is. A good battery (low percentage heteroplasmy) is functioning because it can still generate charge (potential energy).

Did you know that if a pregnant woman's heteroplasmy is high (so her mitochondrial 'batteries' have a low charge), this is passed on to her baby? This will determine the child's baseline immune system and his or her ability to handle exposure to environmental toxins and diseases.

The next key thing to appreciate is that mitochondria DNA signalling turns on and turns off DNA functions in your cell nucleus.[9] Your DNA genome is like your hardware, and your mitochondrial DNA is like your software. There is little we can do to fix our genetic hardware, short of surgery and other medical interventions. However, we can update our mitochondrial software to manage and prevent most of the modern diseases in our world today. If you don't fix deficiencies in heteroplasmy, it not only leads to diseases like Alzheimer's, but it reduces the chances of the next generation being in good health. We'll be looking at ways to lower your heteroplasmy and updating your mitochondrial software in Part 3 of this book.

I'm not trying to scare you, I just want to inform you so that you can make changes that will maximise your cellular battery levels, so that you and your children can live long healthy lives! This is an opportunity. You must make where you live and how you live a conscious choice, and work with the natural environment.

TWO

Light and dark

'We can now say emphatically that the function of our
entire metabolism is dependent on light.'

—Dr Fritz Albert Popp, International Institute of Biophysics

LET'S go back to our gentleman on the island, enjoying good
health and the outdoor paradise from his balcony. Let's say
he goes back to the city, and like many of us, shields himself from
full-spectrum natural sunlight by wearing sunglasses and sunscreen when he's outside. And he spends hours in an office under
artificial light and with windows that prevent him getting full
natural light.

Now, at first, he might have perfectly normal human
experiences – though when I say 'normal', I don't mean 'good'. He's
still eating right and exercising, but he starts to have trouble
sleeping, despite feeling exhausted.[10] He may start to suffer from
headaches and migraines. He might find himself feeling extra
hungry and eating larger portions at mealtimes, even when he's

had enough. Now, these are seemingly non-catastrophic symptoms and behaviours. But over time, research and historical data demonstrate that he will likely eventually suffer from illnesses such as cancer,[11] diabetes,[12] heart disease or obesity[13].

Why is artificial light bad?

Dr Charles Czeisler of Harvard Medical School showed, in 1981, that daylight (full-spectrum sunlight) keeps a person's internal biological clock aligned with the environment.[14] If you throw it out of sync, you throw your body out of sync.

At night, being exposed to artificial light throws the biological clock out of sync.[15] Think of it like this: if you were swimming and breathed in while your head was submerged, you would cough and splutter, reducing your ability to swim smoothly and properly. Do it often enough, and you would have lungfuls of water and wouldn't be able to keep swimming. It's the same thing with your body clock. If you put it out of sync enough, myriad necessary functions will be impaired.

Living a modern life with little or no access to sunlight and excessive artificial light decouples our connection to the ultimate power source of this planet (the sun) and ruins our cells' ability to function properly.

Dr Jack Kruse, the neurosurgeon, pioneer of quantum biology and health educator I mentioned in the introduction, mapped the mechanics behind why shielding ourselves from natural sunlight and drowning ourselves in artificial lighting harms us. In his article 'The Dark Night',[16] Kruse explains that when the UV light is absent, we age faster. This is because we lose a part of the electrical signal that is normally converted by the retina and used to regulate other body processes by generating melatonin.

Consequently, we lose energy, which means we degrade both physically, emotionally and mentally.

Obesity

A study published by The *International Journal of Obesity*[17] found that bright artificial lights which glare all night may be related to nearby residents being overweight. The team at the University of Haifa in Israel found a statistically significant correlation between a man or a woman being overweight or obese and the person living near artificial light at night.

So what is actually happening? Melatonin is suppressed by blue light from artificial lights, computer and TV screens, and by lack of full spectrum sunlight. Melatonin normally suppresses or decreases a person's sensitivity to leptin, a hormone that helps regulate appetite. This results in you being unable to feel satiated,[18] despite having high energy stores. Put simply, you feel hungrier and consume more than your body needs, despite your body having all the energy stores it requires!

Insomnia

Blue light suppresses melatonin, but it also stimulates cortisol production. This is useful during the daytime when cortisol is supposed to be high and melatonin low to keep you alert. However, at night, when melatonin is supposed to be high and cortisol is supposed to be low, artificial light from digital screens, building lights and car headlights disrupts your natural circadian rhythm. It's easy to see why insomnia is endemic in developed countries.

Insomnia and obesity are also related. Try sleeping in artificial lighting for days, weeks or months. What you will find is that as your sleep suffers, your body will degrade and you will crave compensation for that in the form of indulgent foods.

Other illnesses

Research published in the *Journal of Clinical Endocrinology & Metabolism* states, frighteningly, that 'exposure to certain types of electric light before bed and at night can increase the risk of type 2 diabetes, high blood pressure and cancer.'

Dr Kruse estimates that if your heteroplasmy is around 30 per cent, you may become prone to diabetes, and if it continues to rise you are at increased risk of developing Alzheimer's or another neurodegenerative disease. Remember, 'high percent heteroplasmy' means poor cell condition and a low 'battery level', and low percent heteroplasmy means good cell condition and well-charged batteries.

Dopamine

Dopamine is one of my favourite chemicals – it's the neurotransmitter most responsible for drive, motivation, attention, decision-making and learning. It keeps us motivated to learn, make choices and survive.

Although dopamine can be made chemically or taken as a supplement, many side effects result from this. Dopamine is optimally produced by exposure to ultraviolet light from the sun. Now, reports from the US Environmental Protection Agency show that average Americans spend 93 per cent of their lives indoors.[19] This means they only spend 7 per cent or a half-day per week outdoors. That's nowhere near enough exposure sunlight to generate the necessary levels of dopamine.

Worse still, many people work in front of LED computer

screens and mobile device screens inside offices lit with LED or fluorescent lighting that emit excessive amounts of blue light. Chronic bright light exposure reduces dopamine neurons and has been implicated in the development of Parkinson's disease.[20]

It's not just humans

Light pollution doesn't just affect humans, either – it poses ecological problems too. For example, streetlights near shorelines can cause baby turtles who have just hatched to become disoriented and wander inland instead of into the ocean, causing them to die because of dehydration or exposure to predators.[21]

Flicking on the lights – a little history lesson

If we take a brief walk into history, we can see that in the past, lack of full-spectrum light has had negative health effects – which were treated successfully with full-spectrum light exposure. During the 18th century, a time of massive industrialisation, coal was burnt for power and heating, creating smog that blocked access to full-spectrum sunlight in cities.[22] High-rise and narrow apartments jam-packed humans together, too, further reducing access to light.

The 'diseases of darkness' subsequently emerged, including rickets and tuberculosis (TB). Rickets is a bone disease caused by lack of vitamin D (or other minerals), while tuberculosis is an infectious disease, immunity to which may be turned on by vitamin D. Prior to the discovery of antibiotics, TB was treated using exposure to sunlight by doctors such as Auguste Rollier, whose first 'Sun Clinic' was in Leysin, Switzerland.[23] At the peak of his career, he operated 36 clinics.

Interestingly, according to Alexander Wunsch, as of 2014, more than 30 per cent of the world's population had tuberculosis – latent or active. In many ways, we live in an age of darkness masked by artificial light.

Before artificial lighting, the sun was the major source of lighting, and people spent their evenings in darkness broken only by firelight or candlelight. Today, we're saturated with artificial light. You can't avoid it at night, or even, often, during the day. Look around you and notice how much of your life relies on artificial lighting – whether that's house lighting, computer monitors, televisions, smart phones, traffic and city lights. It's embedded in our society; we're reliant on it. Addicted even. And we're also shielded from natural sunlight by glasses, sunglasses, windows and high-rise commercial buildings.

Did you know why blue LEDs (light-emitting diodes) became so popular? Because they were initially expensive and tricky to make and to buy, which gave them extra caché in the marketplace! The group of people who invented them simply thought they 'looked cool' without considering the biological effects at all.[24] Every product designer wanted to use them. Well, they got the cool thing they wanted. Little did they know that this coolness came with a side serve of suffering for many worldwide.

Losing the stars

If you look up at the evening sky, there's a good chance you won't be able to see what your grandmother saw when she was a little girl. That's because we're shrouded in an artificial haze of light. More than 80 per cent of the world and more than 99 per cent of US and European populations live under light-polluted skies. Light pollution hides the Milky Way from more than a third of humanity, including 60 per cent of Europeans and nearly 80 per cent of North Americans.[25]

There are still a few patches of pristine dark sky left in the world, however, and luckily for me many of them are in Australia with its vast continent and sparse population. My ultimate spot for star-gazing is the Uluru area, deep within the red centre of the Australian outback. Uluru is sacred to the Anangu, the indigenous people of the area, and the beauty of the stars here is nothing short of breath-taking. I often tell my friends in the US and Europe that the reason their skies are bare is because Australia stole most of the stars from them.

The Milky Way is laid out before you; the Orion and Pleiades systems look so close. The local storytellers here recount Dreamtime legends of 'creation time', and stories that our ancestors came from the stars resonate more deeply with me than the ones we grew up believing, that we evolved from apes! No words can describe the feeling, for me, of gazing at the stars here. To lose it would be like losing part of myself.

> This is a huge cultural loss with unforeseeable consequences in the future generations – pristine night skies are a precious merchandise.
>
> —*Fabio Falchi*

Slip, Slop, Slap – but what about skin cancer?

Today, if someone goes outdoors, they are taught to avoid the sun. The Cancer Council in Australia has very successfully used advertising campaigns like *Slip, Slop, Slap* to promote shielding yourself from full-spectrum sunlight in order to prevent skin cancer. 'Slip on a shirt, slop on sunscreen and slap on a hat', right? The campaign is widely credited as playing a key role in the dramatic shift in sun protection attitudes and behaviour over the past three decades since it was launched in 1981, and still embodies the core message of the Cancer Council's SunSmart program.

Most Australians would consider this to be one of the most successful health campaigns in Australia's history, to protect against sun damage. But it did the exact opposite! A study in 2009 found that 87 per cent of Australian dermatologists were seriously deficient in vitamin D (<20 ng/ml) at the end of summer.[26]

And in spite of the success of this and other sun-awareness campaigns, melanoma of the skin – the deadliest form of skin cancer – is currently the third most commonly diagnosed cancer in both males and females in Australia.[27]

What's going on? Bernard Ackerman, MD, one of the world's foremost authorities on the subject of skin cancer and the sun, reports:

> ... the link between melanoma and sun exposure is unproven. There's no conclusive evidence that sunburns lead to cancer. There is no real proof that sunscreens protect against melanoma. There's no proof that increased exposure to the sun increases the risk of melanoma.[28]

Until I did the research for this book, I didn't know that most melanomas occur on the least sun-exposed areas of the body.[29] People of African and Asian descent get melanoma almost exclusively on skin that is not exposed to sunlight – palms, soles, nails and mucous membranes. Not only that, but further sun exposure *decreases* the risk of melanoma[30] – prolonged sun exposure resulted in a 60 per cent increase in survival in patients with malignant melanoma.

Now, the evidence is overwhelming that excessive sun exposure over a lifetime increases the risk of squamous cell carcinoma, but this is a very much less serious cancer. A major study conducted by researchers at the Karolinska Institute in

Sweden found that women who avoid sunbathing during the summer are twice as likely to die as those who sunbathe every day. Researchers concluded that the conventional dogma, which advises avoiding the sun at all costs and slathering on sunscreen to minimise sun exposure, is doing more harm than actual good.[31]

Elizabeth Plourde, PhD, goes further in her book *Sunscreens – Biohazard: Treat as Hazardous Waste*. She extensively documents the serious life-threatening dangers of sunscreens to both people and the environment as well. She provides proof that the incidence of malignant melanoma and all other skin cancers increased significantly with ubiquitous sunscreen use over a 30-year period. She emphasises that many sunscreens contain chemicals that are known carcinogens and endocrine-disrupters.

According to Jack Kruse, in the 1930s and 1940s, there were next to no cases of ocular melanoma. However, today it's the fastest-growing form of eye cancer. Why? Maybe because every man, woman and child is wearing sunglasses and blocking full-spectrum light from their eyes.

So, it seems we have things backwards. The right amount of sunlight actually promotes healing and enhances your bodily defences against cancer.

How did we get it so wrong?

So where did the story that sun is such a bad idea originally came from? According to Dr John Ott, the original papers can be found in ophthalmology. Researchers found some damage caused by UV light – in an uncontrolled blue-light hospital environment! – and concluded that UV exposure from sunlight was bad. Could it be that the artificial light was in fact causing the damage, not the sunlight?

Our sun has been demonised for over 40 years, largely unchallenged. Yet sunlight may actually be one of the most important tools in the medicine bag of life.

Vitamin D

Not only does the UVA in sunlight produce dopamine and set your circadian rhythm for good sleep, the body uses the UVB rays in sunlight to convert cholesterol into vitamin D3. Among other things, Vitamin D3 is protective of cancer. Dr Plourde's book has a chapter on the importance of vitamin D3 to health, and she posits that the current widespread vitamin D3 deficiency is linked to overuse of sunscreen combined with sun avoidance in general.

Vitamin D deficiency is a significant public health issue in Australia and New Zealand. An estimated 31 per cent of adults in Australia have inadequate vitamin D status, increasing to more than 50 per cent in women during winter to spring and in people residing in southern states.[32]

The amount of sunlight required for adequate vitamin D levels depends on a range of factors, including UV level, length of exposure and an individual's skin type. The Cancer Council recommends limiting your exposure to the sun when the UV level is above 3 – for me, living in Sydney, that would mean I would have to cover my entire body or stay indoors almost all day in summer, and from mid-morning to mid-afternoon in spring and autumn. I'm not a doctor and don't give medical advice but I disagree with that.

Sure, it's important to build up skin colour (melanin levels) gradually to avoid damage – that's why when a person lives in the tropics for many years, they don't sunburn anymore. Light-skinned people should ensure their skin does not go past pink to red. Pink is caused by your red blood cells coming to the surface to absorb the sunlight, while red is a burn starting.

Waking up

You may be sitting there thinking, 'But I feel pretty healthy, Jason, and I haven't really had any chronic problems to date. And I've worked in an office for years! I stay up late and I absolutely love looking at the screens of my electronic devices. This must be a joke!'

Surely, if this whole artificial light and disconnection from the sun was a serious problem, people would be talking about it much more, right? The medical professions and the government would be issuing warnings! No. The full repercussions of the research findings have not hit home for many – even highly respected medical professionals with a focus on holistic health. I have two applied science degrees in environmental health (one with a major in toxicology), and I certainly wasn't taught about this at university!

However, slowly and surely, people are waking up to the issue, and doing the best they can with the information they have. GE Lighting acknowledged in a December 2014 white paper that the link between light and melatonin production is well accepted in the scientific community.[33] GE is now committed to 'new innovations... and solutions that help mimic natural light patterns, since they may help to put the body back into, and maintain, its natural circadian rhythm'.

The American Medical Association recently adopted guidance for communities on selecting LED lighting options to minimise potential harmful human and environmental effects.[34] 'Despite the energy efficiency benefits, some LED lights are harmful when used as street lighting,' said AMA board member Maya A. Babu, MD, MBA. 'The new AMA guidance encourages proper attention to optimal design and engineering features when converting to LED lighting that minimize detrimental health and environmental effects.' The guidance strengthens the AMA's policy stand against light pollution and public awareness of the adverse health and environmental effects of pervasive night-time lighting.

It's in the right direction, but we have a way to go. We have to continually innovate ways to fuse the disciplines of our well-being and technological advancement of our race. That way, it works to support life, rather than work against it.

The research regarding the adverse implications of artificial lighting and shielding from the sun is coherent, so I invite you to get more curious, and never stop learning about health from a biophysics perspective. And think about it. Do you wait until you're sure, until you do have a chronic illness? Or do you take some simple measures now to manage the risk and protect your health, and the health of those dear to you?

As the founder of one of Australia's largest environmental consultancy companies, I was kicking myself when I realised I'd been in the dark on the artificial light issue. I always understood that our environment was important for our well-being – I knew it when I campaigned about beach pollution, and when I discovered lead was poisoning our children and pets in Sydney. But I had no idea that light played such a pivotal role in regulating our bodily processes!

Had I known 20 years ago what I know now, I could have delivered my mother a much better quality of life and possibly even turned her condition around. It's obvious to me now that her heteroplasmy was high and her indoor, artificially lit lifestyle was contributing to her poor health. The solution was there all along! I was livid when I realised this – but who's to blame? It's not really anyone's fault. The adverse implications of technologies are not always intended: they're simply often discovered a bit too late. We just don't know what we don't know.

I decided to channel my anger into something positive – this book and my new educational platform, EMF Warriors.

But enough of the history, and the 'how'. What does this mean for your life? For today and the future? We know the problem so we are a step closer to the solution. There are ways to get around it. Could it be as simple as getting more full-spectrum natural light? Maybe. But let's not jump the gun on the solution.

It certainly wouldn't be easy to live in this day and age without ever looking at a computer or TV screen. And try going to work and telling your boss, 'I refuse to work in the office. It's not good for my health' – good luck with that!

Of course, if you're lucky enough to find your idyllic cabin perched on a hill over the sea, on fertile land, and you never want to explore the rest of the world again – go for it! I wish you the best of life and longevity. Likely, that isn't you, though. Likely, it's not anyone you know! Advances in technology have given us so many new choices and conveniences that a 'tree-hugging hippy' doesn't have. Without the internet, for example, we wouldn't be able to access real-time data to make better decisions, look at the weather, find out where the person we're meeting is, communicate by email, see how to get somewhere, store information, or store precious memories. Technology provides wonderful solutions for us!

But then there is a dark side. Now that we are aware, we can use technology in order to aid us in understanding the impact our innovations have on human well-being. The fact is, with technology, we should be able to understand this faster and design homes, spaces and technologies that promote our well-being. And as we'll discover in Part 3, people have already taken steps in this direction, designing with human well-being in mind.

So, we've discussed the artificial light and shielding issue. We now need to look at the other half of the problem. Because think about any device you use these days with a screen, and you'll find it uses wireless technologies. And the invisible electromagnetic energies involved have problematic effects on our health in the same way that artificial lighting does. Once you understand both, you have the two pillars from which you can start piecing together the solutions that are right for you, and for those you care about.

Part summary

- **See and feel things naturally**, as we are meant to do. Natural, full-spectrum sunlight absorbed in moderation through the eyes and skin helps regulate and sustain proper body processes. It produces the electricity that we need to power our cells. We are literally batteries.

- **Trees and human beings are similar.** If you look at a tree and what conditions promote its health, you will understand the simplest and most powerful principles for lasting health. Remember, you don't just consume nutrients and get exercise – you digest light. And the right lighting at the right times is critical to your well-being.

- **Full-spectrum light is obtained from the unfiltered sun.** That means without windshields, window panes, sunscreen, clothing, spectacles or sunglasses in the way.

- **Artificial lighting** disrupts the natural distribution of light and therefore disrupts the bodily processes that the cycle of full-spectrum sunlight and darkness supports.

- **Anything that is a medicine can also be a poison.** Too much sunlight can be a bad thing. Technology can be both beneficial to our health, and detrimental. Be aware of the ways in which artificial environments may be causing you suffering.

- **Technology isn't the enemy.** All our innovations in technology *must*, however, consider the well-being of the environment and the human race. Health and technological progression can't be separate.

- **Wake up** – not just to get sunlight in the morning but also to increase your awareness. Educate yourself, apply what you learn in your own life, and communicate it to the important people in your life. Don't trust everything I say. Do your own research. Think broadly.

- **Congratulate yourself on all your efforts to live well so far.** Whether you've tried hard to eat well, you have exercised regularly, or done meditation or the like – nothing you've done has gone to waste. It has all helped you understand how the environment affects your quality of life, just as your choices can affect the environment. The fact that you're reading this book and taking the initiative to educate yourself puts you ahead of most people!

---

1 John N. Ott, 1973, *Health and Light*, p. 18, Devin-Adair Publishing Company.
2 Jack Kruse, 2015, *Ubiquitination 17: Gears of the "Eye Clock"*, <https://www.jackkruse.com/ubiquitination-17-gears-of-the-eye-clock/>
3 Roland Van Wijk, 2014, *Light in Shaping Life: Biophotons in Biology and Medicine*, Meluna.
4 Jack Kruse, 2016, *Time #7: The Photoelectric Effect*, <https://www.jackkruse.com/time-7-photoelectric-effect/>
5 John N. Ott, 1973, *Health and Light*, p. 18, Devin-Adair Publishing Company.
6 Maurice Ghaly, Dale Teplitz, *The Biologic Effects of Grounding the Human Body During Sleep as Measured by Cortisol Levels and Subjective Reporting of Sleep, Pain, and Stress*, The Journal of Alternative and Complementary Medicine Volume 10, Number 5, 2004, pp. 767–776.
7 Douglas Cecil Wallace is a geneticist and evolutionary biologist at the University of Pennsylvania and the Children's Hospital of Philadelphia in Pennsylvania. He pioneered the use of human mitochondrial DNA as a molecular marker.
8 Wallace DC, 2013, *A mitochondrial bioenergetic etiology of disease.* J Clin Invest., The American Society for Clinical Investigation.
9 Jack Kruse, 2015, *Ubiquitination 17: Gears of the "eye clock"*, <https://www.jackkruse.com/ubiquitination-17-gears-of-the-eye-clock/>
10 *How Light Pollution May Interfere with Your Sleep*, American Academy of Neurology, 68th Annual Meeting in Vancouver, Canada, April 15 to 21, 2016 <https://www.aan.com/PressRoom/Home/PressRelease/1441>

11 Richard G. Stevens et al, 2007, Meeting Report: The Role of Environmental Lighting and Circadian Disruption in Cancer and Other Diseases Environmental Health Perspectives Vol. 115, No. 9, p. 1357-1362.
12 Zelinski, EL, 2014. *The trouble with circadian clock dysfunction: Multiple deleterious effects on the brain and body*, Neuroscience and Biobehavioral Reviews 40.
13 Harvard Health Publications, *Blue light has a dark side*, <http://www.health.harvard.edu/staying-healthy/blue-light-has-a-dark-side>
14 Czeisler CA, Richardson GS, Zimmerman JC, Moore-Ede MC, Weitzman ED, 1981, *Entrainment of human circadian rhythms by light-dark cycles: a reassessment*, Photochem Photobiol.
15 Kozaki T, Kubokawa A, Taketomi R, Hatae K, 2016, *Light-induced melatonin suppression at night after exposure to different wavelength composition of morning light*, Neurosci Lett.
16 Jack Kruse, 2016, *Time #9: The "Dark Knight" of regeneration?* <https://www.jackkruse.com/the-dark-knight/>
17 Rybnikova, NA, Haim, A, Portnov, BA, 2016, *Does artificial light-at-night exposure contribute to the worldwide obesity pandemic?* International Journal of Obesity.
18 The feeling of being full and fed.
19 N.E. Klepeis, W.C. Nelson, WR Ott et al, 2016, *The National Human Activity Pattern Survey (NHAPS): a resource for assessing exposure to environmental pollutants*, Journal of Exposure Science and Environmental Epidemiology Volume 26, No 4.
20 Romeo S, Viaggi C, Di Camillo D, 2013, *Bright light exposure reduces TH-positive dopamine neurons: implications of light pollution in Parkinson's disease epidemiology*, Scientific Reports.
21 Sea Turtle Conservancy, *Information About Sea Turtles: Threats from Artificial Lighting*, <http://www.conserveturtles.org/seaturtleinformation.php?page=lighting>
22 Alexander Wunsch, MD, 2014, *Why the Sun is Necessary for Optimal Health*, Wismar University of Applied Sciences, Germany.
23 Rollier wrote an influential book called *Heliotherapy*. For more about sun therapy in history, I recommend you look up Alexander Wunsch's research presentation, 'Why the sun is necessary for optimal health'.
24 Texyt Staff Reporter, 2007, *Blue LEDs: A health hazard?*, <http://texyt.com/bright+blue+leds+annoyance+health+risks>
25 Fabio Falchi et al, 2016, *The New World Atlas of Artificial Night Sky Brightness Science Advances*, Vol. 2, No. 6.
26 D. Czarnecki, C. J. Meehan and F. Bruce, 2009, *The vitamin D status of Australian dermatologists*, Clinical and Experimental Dermatology, 34: 624–625.
27 Cancer Council, *Skin cancer incidence and mortality*, <http://wiki.cancer.org.au/skincancerstats/Skin_cancer_incidence_and_mortality#cite_note-Citation:Australian_Institute_of_Health_and_Welfare_2014_2-4>
28 Gina Kolata, 2004, *I Beg to Differ; A Dermatologist Who's Not Afraid to Sit on the Beach*, The New York Times.
29 Michael Holick PhD, MD, 2011, *The Vitamin D Solution A 3-Step Startegy to Cure Our Most Common Health Problem*, Plume.
30 Cornelius Kennedy et al. *The Influence of painful sunburns and lifetime sun exposure on the risk of actinic keratosis, seborrheic warts, melanocytic nevi, atypical nevi and skin cancer*, J Invest Dermatol 120:1087-1093, 2003

31 Johan Westerdahl, Christian Ingvar, Anna Måsbäck and Håkan, 2000, *Sunscreen use and malignant melanoma*, Olsson International Journal of Cancer.
32 Daly RM et al, 2011, *Prevalence of vitamin D deficiency and its determinants in Australian adults aged 25 years and older: a national, population-based study*, Clinical Endocrinology (Oxf).
33 REF December 2014 GE Lighting, *Lighting and Sleep*, General Electric Company.
34 American Medical Association Press Release, 2016, *AMA Adopts Community Guidance to Reduce the Harmful Human and Environmental Effects of High Intensity Street Lighting*. <http://www.ama-assn.org/ama/pub/news/news/2016/2016-06-14-community-guidance-street-lighting.page>

PART TWO

ELECTRI-FRIED

'...it turns out that most living things are fantastically sensitive to vanishingly small EMF exposures. The problem is man-made electromagnetic exposures aren't normal.'

—*B. Blake Levitt, award-winning journalist and editor of* Cell Towers: Wireless Convenience? or Environmental Hazard?

THREE

Drowning in waves

'I have no doubt in my mind that at the present time,
the greatest polluting element in the earth's environment is
the proliferation of electromagnetic fields. I consider that to be
far greater on a global scale than warming, and the increase
in chemical elements in the environment.'

—*Dr Robert O. Becker, author of* Cross Currents *and* The Body Electric[35]

SURFING is one of Australia's favourite beach activities – not native to Australia, of course, but we love it. And our beaches are some of the finest in the world! But there's one not-so-enjoyable aspect to surfing that any surfer will tell you about – the 'impact zone', the zone where the waves break and crash. If the waves come rolling in and you're in the impact zone – well, it's an effort to get out. You have to duck under the water to avoid being pummelled, and by the time you surface, the next wave may well have arrived to crash on you. The impact zone is where most surfing-related injuries occur.

Unless you're strong, it's hard to get out of the impact zone: weaker surfers will just ride the waves back to shore and call it a day. Beginner surfers who are silly enough to go out on a day of big surf can drown. Keep this metaphor in mind as you read through this chapter, because I believe our addiction to technology is eventually going to feel like being stuck in that impact zone. We *must* be empowered to get out of it.

When I deliver keynote talks, I often ask the audience what they think humanity's greatest challenge is. People generally list things such as climate change, war, genetically modified food, pesticides or (lately) Donald Trump. (I get the sentiment!) But after 30 years of working in environmental health in government and industry I've realised that none of these things is our biggest challenge. As you can probably tell by now, my belief is that addiction to technology (though not technology itself) is our greatest threat and is causing an epidemic of health issues. And with the trends in technology and the exponential rate of change, it's only going to get worse – I'll talk about this more in Part 4, 'Shadows in the future'. It doesn't bode well for you, your loved ones, your children and your children's children.

Yes, I'm presenting this in a way that may scare you a little. A bit of shock wakes you up and helps you become alert and aware!

In Part 1 of this book, we talked about the importance of full-spectrum light, which consists of visible light plus the ultraviolet and infra-red. As you may remember, this is only a small part of the electromagnetic spectrum – yet disruptions to our access to it can cause so many problems! Here in Part 2, we discuss another part of the spectrum that poses an equally great threat – microwaves and radio waves, generated and transmitted by things such as:

- wireless transmission technology, for example wi-fi, 4G, 5G and Bluetooth
- smart meters and devices that send data about your home electricity, gas and water usage.

And these technologies are poised to submerge humanity in their fields.

Figure 3.1 shows you again where radio waves and microwaves sit in the electromagnetic spectrum – outside the visible spectrum, past infra-red in the lower frequencies.

Figure 3.1: Radio waves and microwaves in the electromagnetic spectrum

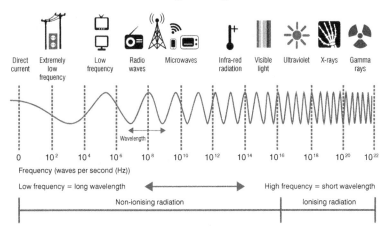

In this book, I refer to the lower frequencies that are not native to this earth and have clearly established biological effects as 'harmful' electromagnetic frequencies (EMFs).

Now, so you're clear, *everything* emits EMFs. The natural world, including your body, produces EMFs, generally ones that are low in intensity. However, modern technology produces

EMFs that our bodies have never encountered before and these fields have health risks.

You can see in Figure 3.1 that the spectrum is divided into higher energy 'ionising' radiation, which can have thermal (heating) effects and lower frequency 'non-ionising' fields, which have non-thermal effects that influence your biology at a more subtle, yet significant level. Some EMFs are healing (e.g. sunlight, grounding, TENS medical devices), but all EMFs, visible and invisible, can be potentially harmful to human biology.

Every-day appliances such as your hair-dryer, fridge and bedside lamp (as well as the 50/60 Hz power lines that provide electricity to these appliances) generate EMFs between 3 Hz and 300 Hz – 'extremely low frequencies' or ELFs. Smartphones, wireless devices and home cordless phones all generate non-ionising radio frequencies (3 KHz to 300 KHz) and microwave radiation generates EMFs between 300 MHz to 300 GHz. Basically, anything that runs on electricity generates potentially harmful EMFs. We have been exposed to ever-increasing levels of man-made EMFs since the days when electricity was first harvested.

But who would have thought all of these things were a threat? Well, plenty of people have over the years, actually, as you will see. The information just hasn't reached you till today. It certainly didn't reach me until recently! I was an undergraduate in environmental science, and I even did an assignment on non-ionising radiation – and we were told radiation was only risky if it had thermal effects. In other words, if it didn't heat you up, it wasn't a problem. That's not true, but it remains the basis for all government exposure standards relating to modern telecommunication devices. Yet, as I will share with you throughout this book, there is a significant body of high-quality, peer-reviewed science that demonstrates that all forms of electromagnetic radiation have observable effects on biological systems.

Except for visible light and infra-red (which can be felt as heat), we cannot perceive EMFs without specially designed instruments. Our bodies are affected, yes, but there are no sensory cues – unless of course you are part of the 1 to 3 per cent of the population who are electro-hypersensitive. So it's not obvious that we have abruptly added large amounts of manmade EMFs (in particular, microwaves) to our environment. Swedish neuro-oncologist Leif Salford has said that we are participating in 'the largest biological experiment ever'.

How the waves built

Let's take another little trip down history lane.

For most of the earth's history, the electromagnetic frequencies were simple. There was the earth's heartbeat, the Schumann resonances[36] – essentially, weak low frequencies generated by static electricity from lightning – and full-spectrum light from our sun, providing abundant amounts of visible light, ultraviolet and infra-red.

But in 1893, things started to change. Nikola Tesla demonstrated the first AC power system at the World's Fair, and Thomas Edison began the first commercial electric company in New York. Just a few years later, the modern electrical era began, bringing lighting and power to homes. The world became electrified – and a suite of mysterious illnesses emerged. Telegraph line installers and telephone switchboard operators suffered nerve disorders, convulsions, depression, anxiety and a whole host of other problems.[37] In 1907, the Bell Telephone switchboard operators in Toronto went on strike over this.

After World War II in the mid-1940s, came the greatest increase in use of shorter wavelength EMFs (microwave and radio waves). In 1947, Bell Telephone set up the first microwave phone relay between Boston and New York City. Then television was born. By the 1950s, radar operators were suffering similar symptoms to the telephone switchboard workers.

Meanwhile, on the other side of the world, the Soviet government started extensive testing of the effects of microwave EMFs on workers and discovered definitive biological effects. They immediately set limits on microwaves for their workers and soldiers and went as far as calling for a meeting with the USA in the middle of the Cold War to discuss their findings.

The American military, unfortunately, dismissed this as an attempt to embarrass the US. So, to prove themselves right, the Russians irradiated the US embassy in Moscow from 1962 to 1969 with 4,000 to 6,000 millivolts of microwaves – what was called 'the Moscow signal'. The Americans did nothing for a decade, then an American scientist named Milton Zaret was hired to examine the effects of the Moscow signal, in what was called Project Pandora.[38] Zaret found that the microwave radiation interfered with embassy workers' decision-making capacity and caused chronic stress and low efficiency. In addition, their white blood cell counts were 40 per cent higher than normal!

It wasn't until 1976 that stories about Project Pandora started circulating in the media. In a documentary from 1984, 'Opening Pandora's Box',[39] American orthopaedic surgeon Dr Becker confesses he couldn't say anything about the issue at the time because it would have been an embarrassment to the American government and an outrage to the embassy employees who found out they were being used as guinea pigs. It's a distressing example of how political pride can trump a government's responsibility to protect its people.

From the mid to late 1960s, papers about 'microwave syndrome' became numerous in Russian scientific literature, describing the links between microwaves and headaches, blurred vision, loss of concentration, poor sleep and so on. In 1971, Zinaida Gordon and Maria Sadchikova of the USSR Institute of Labor Hygiene and Occupational Diseases identified what they called 'microwave sickness', with symptoms including chronic excitation of the sympathetic nervous system. This excitation suppressed sensitivity to leptin, just as artificial lighting does, as we discussed in Chapter 2. The results were adrenal fatigue, ischemic heart disease, atherosclerosis, high blood pressure, high triglycerides, poor sleep and – diabetes.

As a side note: many people view Russia as somewhat behind the West in the technological arena. In 2001, I visited the nickel mine near the world's northernmost city, Norilsk, inside the Arctic Circle, to demonstrate portable X-ray fluorescence technology for underground geochemistry applications. The mine was run down, vehicles had no seat belts, I'm not sure the safety gear worked and there were a host of other safety breaches that would see such a mine closed by the unions in Australia. But never let appearances fool you – the Russians lead the world in energetic medicine and electronic countermeasures (ECM). In 2014, their 'Khibiny' ECM jammer system was purportedly able to shut down the electronic and communications systems of the USS *Donald Cook*, a US naval missile destroyer.[40]

Electromagnetic hypersensitivity

Since the turn of the 21st century, the introduction of wireless technologies such as wi-fi, smartphones, and smart meters has seen a rise in electromagnetic hypersensitivity (EHS). In 2004, the World Health Organization defined EHS as:

'... a phenomenon where individuals experience adverse health effects while using or being in the vicinity of devices emanating electric, magnetic, or electromagnetic fields (EMFs) ... Whatever its cause, EHS is a real and sometimes a debilitating problem for the affected persons ... Their exposures are generally several orders of magnitude under the limits in internationally accepted standards.'[41]

Steve Weller is an IT professional who has been an avid user of computers all his life and discovered quite by accident that he was sensitive to certain harmful EMFs in his early thirties. In late 2001, wireless local area networking (WLAN) was beginning to become popular and Steve loved the idea of having no wires cluttering his desk and being free to work on his laptop at the kitchen table. Being IT-savvy, he purchased the most powerful wi-fi router available at the time. Almost instantly, he began to feel pressure in his head, irregular heartbeats and tingling sensations in his hands and face. His wife noticed that he had become more agitated and short-tempered instead of being his normal relaxed self.

Steve soon realised that a consistent pattern was developing when using his wireless router. The symptoms were real, consistent and unpleasant – this was not psychosomatic. He disconnected his WLAN and hardwired his internet connection and his symptoms lessened and became manageable.

Interestingly, five years later, he purchased a Sony PlayStation 3 and still found his symptoms barely noticeable – the PS3 controller is a wireless Bluetooth device operating at 2.4 GHz, the same as a WLAN router, although at lower power. However, when he purchased a Nintendo Wii for his children for Christmas, his EHS symptoms reappeared. The Wii controllers also use Bluetooth 2.4 GHz – the difference is the amount of data being transmitted. The PS3 controller only sends information when a button is pressed, while the Wii controller continually transmits signals, as it needs to send telemetry data to indicate the position and movement of the controller (to allow users to play, say, virtual tennis). Steve's symptoms were related to the *continual transmission* of harmful EMF signals, rather than the power generated by the devices.

Steve can only use a mobile phone for 30 seconds before feeling severe discomfort and only owns a phone for emergencies. He opted out of the smart meter roll-out – another continuous source of harmful EMFs – but was severely affected by his neighbours' meter, which was located close to his bedroom. He reports waking up regularly feeling as though a long, sharp needle had been pushed into his head. Exposure to other sources of harmful EMFs at his workplace and while travelling took its toll in allergic reactions, constant headaches, extremely lethargy and loss of all motivation.

Unfortunately, Steve's story is not that uncommon and you can read more at www.electroplague.com/ehs-stories. Take an objective look: you will find that the case studies are largely from credible professionals, not crackpots. Here are a few more examples, with links to their stories in the endnotes:

- Brian Stein, CEO of a billion-dollar UK company[42]
- Former Nokia Chief Technology Officer Matti Niemelä[43]
- Physics professor James McCaughan[44]
- Civil and environmental engineer Jeremy Johnson[45]
- General practitioner Dr Elizabeth Evans[46]
- IT professional Richard Kimberley[47]
- Olga Sheean, author, editor and expert in human dynamics[48]
- TV producer Sarah Dacre.[49]

EHS sufferers are brave, unsung heroes. They are usually told by friends, family and the medical profession that they are making their symptoms up and as a result feel extremely isolated and marginalised. EHS is declared to be 'not a medical diagnosis' by the World Health Organization, and so sufferers' symptoms are often ignored by government health authorities and misdiagnosed by the medical profession, which can then lead to the prescription of unnecessary and ineffective medication.

Sweden, however, recognises EHS as a functional impairment, while the Austrian Medical Association has provided guidelines on EHS diagnosis and treatment.[50] Some countries, like the US and UK, have merely labelled it a 'condition'. In Russia, EHS would be diagnosed as microwave sickness: the Russians are serious about the problem and have built shielded rooms in hospitals for EHS patients.

It may not be a widely recognised condition, but the incidence of EHS is increasing at an alarming rate. In 2006, health researchers Örjan Hallberg and Gerd Oberfeld estimated[51] that by 2017, 50 per cent of the population is likely to be electrically sensitive. One of the foremost experts on EHS, Dr Magda Havas, estimates that perhaps 3 per cent of the population have severe EHS symptoms and that 35 per cent of the population have mild to moderate symptoms. If we apply these percentages to a few countries, as shown in Table 3.1, the number of people already affected is staggering.

Table 3.1: Number of people with EHS symptoms

	Population	Severe (3%)	Mild/moderate (35%)
Australia	23 million	0.7 million	8 million
Canada	35 million	1.1 million	12 million
USA	319 million	10 million	112 million
Europe	741 million	22 million	259 million

The numbers seem excessive, until you think about how many people you know suffer from mild to moderate EHS symptoms such as headaches, sleeping problems and fatigue. Could harmful EMFs really be an underlying cause of these common symptoms? We will investigate this further over the next chapters.

Dirty electricity – the wake-up call

What really catalysed global awareness of harmful EMFs was a book released in 2010 by physician and epidemiologist Dr Samuel Milham, called *Dirty Electricity: Electrification and the diseases of civilization.* In the book, Dr Milham goes into detail about the history of the effects harmful EMFs have had on humanity. He analysed the death records of electrified and rural areas in the early part of the 20th century and compared them with statistics from areas where there was no electrification. He discovered a correlation between electrification and the incidences of conditions such as cancer, diabetes, heart disease and neurodegenerative disease, as well as suicide.

What he discovered was that many electronic devices (computers, televisions and the like) chop up the electricity your house receives from the substation, and in doing so, add high-frequency currents to the return current. This current is way above the levels that the wires can safely handle. But the current *has* to be returned to the substation. Fixing the issue would involve installing multiple wires, which would be costly. So in the last 20 years in the USA, the 'dirty electricity' has been dumped into the earth, where it gets into homes via the ground wires and metal plumbing. As Dr Milham put it, it is 'electricity that shouldn't be there'.

One quick and easy way to get an idea of whether you have dirty electricity in your household wiring is to use a battery powered AM radio. Tune the radio to the white noise between the stations and move around your home, holding it near your electrical power outlets. If your radio gives extra hiss as you do this, it's an indication that dirty electricity is present.

If you want to satisfy the nerd within and learn more about the specifics, I suggest you read Dr Milham's book. He really is a hero for his contributions to the body of knowledge about harmful EMFs. I don't 100 per cent agree with his conclusion that the 20th century's epidemic of cardiovascular diseases, cancers, suicide, diabetes and obesity has been caused by electricity. I believe artificial lighting and our shielding from the sun have also had a key part to play. But it is worth a read.

The waves get ever-bigger

Here's a scary summation of our history lesson. Technology applications over the last century have been moving up the EMF spectrum, increasing in frequency and energy. The start of the

20th century saw the roll-out of ELF-generating AC power. The introduction of radio added the radio frequency range. Television, radar, mobile phones and wi-fi networks use even higher frequency microwave radiation. We find ourselves bombarded by more and more harmful EMFs from more sources across a broader section of the electromagnetic spectrum. And as we will discuss in Part 4, the rate of change is not slowing down.

So, was it intentional? Did someone just decide one day, 'Hey! Let's invent technologies specifically to cause disease to humanity'? I personally believe that engineers simply think of cost-effective ways to roll out technology and fail to think about biology.

For example, did you know that iPhones have some hidden safety advice? If you go to the settings and then to 'General', 'About', 'Legal', and 'RF Exposure', you will find the following statement, 'iPhone has been tested and meets applicable limits for radio frequency (RF) exposure'. (You can find similar warnings for other phones at www.showthefineprint.org.) The problem is, what this is talking about is the non-thermal effects of RF on human biology and the Specific Absorption Rate (SAR) standard is 20 years old! We are using outdated standards, which some say are virtually useless for rapidly evolving technology. Also, SAR is good for measuring electromagnetic radiation, but as a safety standard it's fundamentally flawed – the SAR of your phone doesn't translate to how much radiation you're actually exposed to. Tests assume you hold the phone at a precise angle and don't take into consideration your exposure when the phone is on but not in use. Remember, unless your phone is turned off or in aeroplane mode, it is in constant contact with telecommunication towers and wi-fi routers.

Still, let's look at what Apple says about SAR on the iPhone 6:

> To reduce exposure to RF energy, use a hands-free option, such as the built-in speakerphone, the supplied headphones, or other similar accessories. **Carry iPhone at least 5mm away from your body to ensure exposure levels remain at or below the as-tested levels.** Cases with metal parts may change the RF performance of the device, including its compliance with RF exposure guidelines, in a manner that has not been tested or certified.
>
> Although this device has been tested to determine SAR in each band of operation, not all bands are available in all areas. Bands are dependent on your service provider's wireless and roaming networks.[52]

This essentially means that Apple advises you not to keep the phone in your pocket or touching your skin. And so many people hold their phones right up against their ear and carry them in their chest pockets or back or front trouser pockets – some women even like to carry their phone in their bra. But Apple is getting there. The iPhone 3GS's safety limit was 15 mm and the iPhone 4 and 5's was 10 mm. At this rate, maybe by the time the iPhone 10 comes out, holding it in our hands will be safe!

Again, this isn't necessarily the result of someone's evil agenda. The human race just doesn't bother to investigate the effects of new technologies before rolling them out on a global scale! To me, it's a symptom of the way we have ignored the connection between our environment and our health.

As I mentioned in the introduction, when I began studying the effects of the environment on human health, I was in my late teens and I enrolled in an applied science degree in environmental health and graduated in 1988. Back then, the New South Wales government acknowledged the interrelationship between pollution and human disease. The State Pollution Control Commission (SPCC) was focused on discharge licensing and controlling emissions from industry; the Health Department, where I worked, focused on environmental health as part of the overall public health framework. The legacy of John Snow lived on. (No, not the bastard son of Ned Stark in *Game of Thrones*, but Dr John Snow, one of the fathers of epidemiology. In the 1850s, Dr Snow traced the source of a cholera outbreak in Soho, London to contaminated water and highlighted the importance of improving sanitation.)

Unfortunately in the early 1990s, New South Wales replaced the SPCC with the Environment Protection Authority (EPA) and many of the environmental health roles were lost or transferred to local government. Environmental health officers in the NSW Department of Health essentially became researchers for the newly established public health units. The interrelationship between the environment and health was no longer reflected in the government structure, and NSW Department of Health became focused on hospital admissions while NSW EPA focused on flora and fauna.

This division between health and the environment is also evident in the health profession, where nutrition is barely a subject in a four-year medical degree and the healing powers of full-spectrum sunlight are rarely mentioned. Well-being isn't part of the curriculum in schools and universities, either! I have a postgraduate degree in environmental health and I was never taught about mitochondrial DNA and heteroplasmy, or about the effects of excessive blue light on circadian rhythms, or about the importance of UV sunlight for vitamin D production, or about the impact of harmful EMFs. It took me 30 years to find out about it!

The science of environmental health has been lost – it's time for it to be revived. We live in an exciting time when new knowledge is challenging long-held beliefs. Quantum biology is set to turn the medical profession on its head. And new, exciting technologies that integrate nature's frequencies are set to become part of the treatments of the future.

Unfortunately, harmful EMFs aren't just a by-product of modern society, nor are they easily avoided. Our use of EMFs is the cornerstone of modern life. Transport, water supply, food production and storage, banking and health care are all dependent on electric power and wireless communication! So it's not surprising that most people are predisposed to resist information that may challenge the safety of technology that emits harmful EMFs. I get it, I really do! I'm not going to give up my iPhone, iPad and computers – are you?

The reality is, the problem isn't going to go away. It's sad I know, but true. Telecommunication towers emit harmful EMFs 24/7 in order to give our smartphones reception. Smart meters pulse harmful EMFs throughout the day so the electricity companies can monitor our power usage, and our wi-fi routers are permanently on because our teenagers (among others!) think access to the internet is their God-given right. Harmful EMFS are here to stay. These waves are just pounding and pounding, and the sets won't stop coming.

FOUR

The invisible stressor

'Biological reactions can be affected by exposure to
all parts of the spectrum – even in the very low frequency
ELF range. All EMF is bioactive.'

—*Martin Blank, PhD*

REMEMBER our healthy friend from Part 1, enjoying the sunrise from his balcony? For the purposes of this book, let's whisk him away now from his happy existence by the beach and place him in a technologically saturated environment. We will make the following, seemingly insignificant adjustments to his lifestyle:

- Place his wireless internet router in his bedroom and leave it running 24/7
- Place his phone on charge on his bedside table for easy access during the night
- Give him a wireless Bluetooth headset, since that seems safer than putting the phone next to his ear

- Ask him to carry his smartphone in his trouser pocket near his testicles, where it would be touching his skin if not for the sliver of fabric between his flesh and the device
- Have him use his microwave to heat up his dinner and stand in front of the microwave waiting impatiently for it to be cooked, while checking his Facebook account and email on his phone
- Have him work in the city, where telecommunications towers litter the rooftops of multi-storey buildings, a dozen or more wi-fi routers are trying to connect with his smartphone everywhere he goes and wireless signals surround him like the air he breathes – as depicted in the image below.

Figure 4.1: An artistic impression of a wi-fi world

Sounds pretty normal right? These are the times we live in. Look at almost any device we rely on these days and you will find that it emits electromagnetic radiation (EMR), especially in the radio wave and microwave end of the spectrum.

All bands of EMR serve a very useful function for our society and have arguably helped to bring us to our current point of advancement. We are hooked: we love our phones, our wi-fi, our computers and all the convenience of city living, and it would be hard to wean ourselves off these everyday luxuries. We have become addicted to technology.

According to my research, here's what may happen to our healthy gentleman over time in his new environment:

- **His immune system will weaken and he will start getting colds and flus much more often,** taking days, if not weeks, to fully recover.
- **His energy will diminish** and he will find himself fading faster in his city office behind the computer screen.
- **Brain fog will start to set in** and no amount of coffee will clear his head.
- **Headaches will become more frequent, as will ringing in his ears.**
- **He will have problems sleeping and may develop insomnia.** This may lead to chronic tiredness, and before long he won't have much energy to exercise, or do anything much other than work and eat. As mentioned earlier, long-term insomnia puts you at risk of cancer, cardiovascular diseases, diabetes, obesity and even suicide.
- **His rising stress and anxiety levels** may lead to him finding the simplest of cognitive tasks more of an effort – perhaps leading to depression, with the question, 'What the hell is wrong with me?' ringing in his head.

Could his work performance suffer? Yes. Will his relationships be affected? No doubt. Formerly the picture of physical, mental (and presumably financial!) success, he could soon be drowning without knowing why, submerged in invisible electromagnetic waves and poisoned by artificial light.

Calcium, oxidative stress and peroxynitrite – how EMFs affect us

As I mentioned earlier, everyone is affected biologically by harmful EMFs, although the symptoms are very mild or not severe enough to be considered EHS. We are all unique individuals and have varying capacities to deal with EMFs. However, the more we are exposed to, the more energy and effort our bodies have to put in to manage their effects.

Today, millions of individuals suffer from disorders including:

- developmental disorders
- epilepsy
- amyotrophic lateral sclerosis (ALS)
- autoimmune conditions
- multiple sclerosis (MS)
- Parkinson's disease
- stroke
- various forms of dementia
- ADHD
- autism spectrum disorder.

Shockingly these days, more and more children have diabetes, autism, Parkinson's, ADHD and MS.

There is an emerging link between harmful EMFs and the alarming rise in the incidence of autism. Harvard's Dr Martha Herbert has been presenting a new model of autism as a state of overload that comes from many factors affecting the entire body and not just the brain ('total load' theory).[53] In 2013, Dr Herbert and wireless expert Cindy Sage published two papers that outlined a wide range of autism symptoms that match known symptoms of wireless exposure, including genetic damage to sperm, calcium channel mutations, and inflammation.[54]

Basically, harmful EMFs induce a stress response in our cells.[55] Dr Martin Pall has demonstrated that the biological mechanism by which they do this is via opening up cells' voltage gated calcium channels (VGCC), allowing too much calcium to move into cells:

Electromagnetic fields act via activation of voltage gated calcium channels to produce beneficial or adverse effects.[56]

Too much calcium in the cells results in oxidative stress and inflammatory overload, as explained in the Figure 4.2 overleaf. Diseases such as ALS (a neurological disease that attacks the nerve cells), Parkinson's and Alzheimer's are also caused by excessive calcium in the cell.

This is front-page news! When your body is under constant stress it struggles to deal with any other health problems you may be having. You are literally being handicapped at a cellular level – no wonder modern diseases are rising to epidemic levels.

If you have cancer cells in your body, the cancer is more likely to be much more aggressive in the presence of EMF.

—*Associate Professor Dr Magda Havas*[57]

Figure 4.2: EMF activation of VGCCs increases free radical production

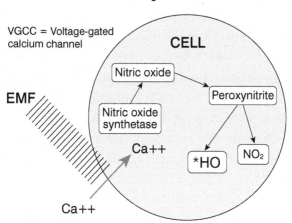

Peroxynitrite produces free radicals, including hydroxyl radical and NO_2. This increase in free radicals then leads to inflammation, oxidant stress and damage to cell structures, including DNA. The EMF doesn't directly damage the cell. It just deranges cellular metabolism. The free radicals that are produced by this change in metabolism are what causes the damages.

Source: Presentation materials of Dr Paul Dart, July 23, 2013, before a special session of the Eugene Water and Electric Board.

Richard Lear has founded five Silicon Valley-based businesses and is currently Managing Director of Vantage Partners, an executive search company. He has an exceptional talent for pattern recognition, and recently published a draft paper putting out a call for one or two PhD scientists to undertake research on the root cause of the dramatic rise of chronic disease.[58]

Richard has mined US government databases and identified 40 diseases that have more than doubled since 1990 – some exponentially. Four categories of disease have virtually exploded: autoimmune, neurological, metabolic and inflammatory. There's been a similar uptick in reproductive conditions like infertility and a half dozen psychiatric disorders. None of these are associated with an identifiable pathogen. The major health threats of the 20th century (cardiovascular disease, infectious disease and cancer) are barely growing, but the increase of these modern diseases in a single generation is staggering, as you can see in the table below. Many weren't even on our radar until the 1980s.

Table 4.1: The increase in disease (1990–2015)

Disease	Increase
Chronic fatigue	11,027%
Bipolar	10,833%
Fibromyalgia	7,727%
Autism	2,094%
Coeliac disease	1,111%
ADHD	819%
Hypothyroidism	720%
Osteoarthritis	449%
Sleep apnoea	430%
Diabetes Mellitus	305%
Alzheimer's	299%
Depression	280%

Source: Richard Lear, 'The Root Cause in the Dramatic Rise of Chronic Disease', Draft, June 2016.

Until now, many in the scientific community have been reticent to propose a unifying factor that could explain the dramatic rise of so many seemingly unrelated diseases. Yet there is growing evidence that the smoking gun could be a chemical called peroxynitrite. There is still controversy over possible external causes, but Lear and leading pharmacology researchers like Dr Pal Pacher strongly feel that peroxynitrite is associated with much of this sudden explosion of disease.[59]

So what's this got to do with harmful EMFs? Lots. Go back and take a close look at Figure 4.2. It shows how harmful EMFs activate the VGCC, disrupting cellular metabolism and producing, guess what, peroxynitrite and nitric oxide, which increases the production of free radicals including hydroxyl and nitric dioxide. This then leads to inflammation, oxidant stress and damage to cell structures, including DNA (which we'll talk about more in the next section). Are you starting to see how the pieces of the jigsaw puzzle come together?

The economic and social impact of these 'new' diseases is substantial. In the USA alone, more than $2.5 trillion is spent annually on the 40 diseases Lear identified, including medical costs, lost income and research. The human suffering and societal costs are incalculable. And the numbers are likely substantially understated – there are hundreds of chronic diseases and medical conditions not tracked in Lear's paper.

For entrepreneurs and advocates for safe technology, Lear's paper and the $2.5 trillion annual cost he identifies is very useful information to share with policy-makers and public health officials.

EMFs damage DNA

Studies also show that all frequencies of EMFs can react with and damage DNA, leading either to cell death or remaining as a mutation, which can lead directly to serious diseases including cancer. Some of the highest quality work on DNA damage from harmful EMFs was conducted by Professor Henry Lai and Dr Narendra Sign at the University of Washington in the mid to late 1990s.[60] Their work showed that exposures of only two hours increased the number of DNA strand breaks in the brain cells of living rats. Their research has been replicated elsewhere, and it has been confirmed that harmful EMFs can damage DNA at levels well below current safety standards.

If you'd like to know more, Dr Martin Blank of Columbia University is arguably the leading authority on EMF–DNA interaction; his book *Overpowered: what science tells us about the dangers of cell phones and other wifi-age devices* is a must-read.

Between the legs

If you ever want to get a man's attention, hit him where it hurts. I used this theory when I was running lead-awareness workshops for a mining company in Broken Hill – an isolated city in outback New South Wales that's home to one of the world's largest silver–lead–zinc mineral deposits. My environmental company had been asked to develop and implement a lead risk-management strategy for the new owners, who were concerned about the risks associated with the purchase of a 100-year-old lead/zinc mine. Part of the strategy was induction training for all 400 staff on how to minimise their lead risk exposure before they commenced work in the mine.

My presentation was part of the company's three-day induction training, and I was given the unenviable task of teaching in the afternoon on the last day. Miners are a tough breed and an even tougher audience, especially after being cooped up in a classroom for three days. I knew the best way to get their attention was to hit them between the legs. I covered all the health effects of lead on adults –potential neurological impairment, high blood pressure, aggression and potential death – but it was the information on erectile dysfunction that got their full attention!

There has been a dramatic rise in male infertility. The data suggests that sperm counts have halved in the past 50 years and are continuing to fall.[61] As many as 7 per cent of men globally are infertile and 45 per cent are sub-fertile.[62] And there is strong data to suggest that harmful EMFs, particularly from mobile phones, are a key source of this infertility. A review of several scientific studies in 2011 concluded that men who used mobile phones experienced 'decreased sperm concentration, motility, abnormal morphology and viability', and similar results were found in laboratory tests.[63] The review also found that the longer a man used a mobile phone, the higher the risk of these abnormalities.

A study published in 2015[64] showed that having a mobile phone close to the testicles could lower sperm levels so much that conceiving could be difficult.

Are you starting to appreciate that carrying your smartphone in your pocket next to your reproductive organs is not such a good idea? If you're carrying your phone on your body for long periods of time, it's best to put it in aeroplane mode, or at least carry it in a side jacket pocket or in your work briefcase or handbag.

FIVE

Do mobile phones really cause cancer?

'I never thought I'd say this in my life, but cell phones are
probably worse than cigarettes for overall health.'

—*Dr Jack Kruse*

DO mobile phones cause cancer? The answer is – probably, if the exposure is close enough, long enough and of sufficient magnitude.[65]

For years, the safety of mobile phones has been debated. On one hand, hundreds of studies show that radio frequency levels hundreds of times lower than those in government safety standards cause damage to biological systems. On the other hand, industry executives and government officials have adhered to what is called a 'thermal paradigm', claiming that RF radiation is not harmful unless it causes physical burns or shock.

The mobile phone industry and government will tell you that

your phone is safe – and we so want to believe them so we can continue our addictive love affair with our phones. But the science suggests otherwise.

In 2009, the *Journal of Clinical Oncology* published the findings of a team of scientists who reviewed 23 epidemiological studies on the link between cell phone use and cancer. They concluded:

> Although as a whole the data varied, among the 10 higher quality studies, we found a harmful association between phone use and tumour risk. The lower quality studies, which failed to meet scientific best practices, were primarily industry funded.

> The 13 studies that investigated cell phone use for 10 or more years found a significant harmful association with tumour risk, especially brain tumours, giving us ample reason for concern about long-term use.[66]

Professor Chapman's study

A 2016 study by Professor Simon Chapman, published by *Cancer Epidemiology*,[67] on the other hand, claims to have proven that mobile phones do *not* cause brain cancer. The study analysed the 29-year history of mobile phone use in Australia and compared it with the incidences of brain cancer reported to the cancer registry. There are a couple of reasons why I believe Professor Chapman's conclusion is overstated.

First of all, the study grouped more than 200 different types of brain cancer into one bundle – when glioma (tumours of the glial cells in the brain) is the type of brain cancer associated with mobile phone use and constitutes about 30 per cent of all brain cancers. Interestingly, most glioma tumours occur in precisely the parts of the brain that absorb most of the microwave radiation emitted or received by phones.

Secondly, proportionally few Australians were heavy users of mobile phones 30 years ago. It's only in the last few years that phones have become ubiquitous and affordable, with the heaviest use occurring in relatively young people. If you're interested in the ongoing arguments for and against Professor Chapman's study, visit www.betweenrockandhardplace.wordpress.com/2016/05/10/professor-simon-chapman-responds.

> If you look at the science on mobile phones and the link with brain cancer, it is quite compelling ... we know that [ionising] radiation causes cancer, but it takes about ten years for it to develop, so we know that EMR (electromagnetic radiation) [from phones] is going to take at least ten years to create brain tumours and possibly longer – fifteen, twenty years.[68]

> —Dr Charlie Teo, world-renowned Australian neurosurgeon

The US National Toxicology Program study

A recently completed two-year, $25 million study by the US National Toxicology Program (NTP) on rats exposed to GSM or CDMA mobile phone signals has shown statistically significant increases in two types of cancer:

1. glioma
2. malignant schwannoma of the heart, a very rare tumour.

None of these tumours were found in the unexposed rats.

The exposures were carefully conducted in such a way that heating would not be a contributing factor. The types of cells that became cancerous in the rats were the identical types that have been shown to develop into tumours in human epidemiological studies. The study is the largest of its kind to date and has undergone extensive reviews – and the consensus is that there's a carcinogenic effect from mobile phone radiation:

> This study should put an end to those who doubt the capacity of non-thermal levels of wireless radiation to cause biological effects including cancer. The study results clearly show that cell phone radiation can cause adverse health effects. The counter argument has no validity.
>
> —*Ronald Melnick, PhD, former lead scientist on the study*[69]

The US Air Force study

The NTP study wasn't, of course, the first randomised controlled trial to find that exposure to non-thermal levels of microwave radiation can cause cancer in rats. A US Air Force study conducted from 1980 to 1982, which was documented in a series of nine technical reports and later published in the peer-reviewed journal *Bioelectromagnetics*,[70] found that 18 per cent of 100 male rats exposed to low-intensity RF–EMF developed cancer.

CTIA research

Even mobile phone industry research in the 1990s showed that mobiles caused brain tumours. Dr George Carlo was the leader of the Cellular Telecommunications Industry Association's (CTIA) $25 million research project, which employed 200 scientists. Dr Carlo held three successive meetings in February 1999: one with the executives of the CTIA; the second with the

Food and Drug Administration's Interagency Working Group, which was chartered with determining the safety of cell phones; and the third with the CTIA Board of Directors. At each meeting, he presented the results of CTIA's own studies. Among the findings Dr Carlo presented were:

- a statistically significant doubling of brain cancer risk
- a statistically significant dose-response risk of acoustic neuroma with more than six years of mobile phone use
- findings of genetic damage in human blood when exposed to cell phone radiation.[71]

The CTIA withdrew funding for the research. The research was terminated because long-term studies were showing leakage of the blood-brain barrier and micronuclei (broken DNA) in blood cells.

The International Agency for Research on Cancer

For a week in May 2011, a Working Group of 31 scientists met at the International Agency for Research on Cancer (IARC) in Lyon, France, to evaluate the carcinogenic effect on humans of radiofrequency electromagnetic fields from mobile phones and other devices. They classified these fields in Group 2B, 'possibly carcinogenic'.

Some researchers, like Dr Devra Davis, now feel the scientific evidence is sufficient to classify mobile phone radiation in Group 2A, as a 'probable' human carcinogen. Others like Dr Lennart Hardell advocate for Group 1 'carcinogenic' classification as the IARC Group 1 criteria for increased risk of glioma and acoustic neuroma has been fulfilled.[72]

How many sick or dead people does it take to constitute sufficient proof?

—*Professor Devra Davis, University of Pittsburgh Cancer Institute*

Is it a risk worth taking?

As Dr Carlo states in his 2002 book *Cell Phones: invisible hazards in the wireless age: an insider's alarming discoveries about cancer and genetic damage*:

> The big picture is disturbingly clear. There is a definite risk that the radiation plume that emanates from a cell phone antenna can cause cancer and other health problems. It is a risk that must be seen and understood by all who use cell phones so they can take all the appropriate and available steps to protect themselves and especially to protect young children whose skulls are still growing and who are the most vulnerable to the risks of radiation.

The Australian Radiation Protection and Nuclear Safety Agency (ARPANSA) is wisely hedging its bets. Although they maintain a staunch stance on the minimal (if any) effects of harmful EMFs, they recommend taking precautions to minimise unnecessary exposure, especially to children (for details, see Part 3).

Here's the rub. There are now almost as many mobile phone subscriptions in the world as there are people – over seven billion in use![73] They are everywhere. And almost every user carries their mobile phones with them; many even take them to bed.

The debate continues, but I would really like to see the naysayers enrol their kids as the test subjects for the next longitudinal study on the effects of mobile phones!

SIX

Smart meters – not so intelligent

'A smart grid that is as vulnerable as ours is not smart
at all it's a really, really stupid grid.'

—*James Woolsey, former CIA Director*

S O what about smart meters? I think it's worth discussing them, so you understand just how bombarded with EMFs you are by these conveniences of life. What's a smart meter? I've included a picture of one in Figure 6.1 overleaf. It's an electronic device that records the consumption of electrical energy, gas and water in your house. It wirelessly communicates the information to the utility company, which then bills you. It's much simpler than having someone walk around to every house and check the meter – great idea, right?

Not really. Smart meters, now being rolled out to millions of homes across the country, are part of a smart neighbourhood grid and mesh network that allows two-way communications between an electric utility and you. Now, let me explain exactly how that system works and why there are problems with it. Eventually, what will happen is that all of your appliances will have embedded antennae that will communicate with your smart meter – your microwave oven, your regular oven, your washer, your dryer, your computer, your television, your coffee machine, your air conditioners – every appliance that uses electricity. The meter will transmit wirelessly at a slightly higher frequency to a central hub, which will gather the information for billing purposes and load requirements for the electrical grid.

Figure 6.1: A smart meter

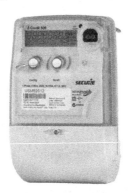

All this technology relies on harmful EMFs. And what happens with smart meters is that you can get aggregate exposure from one signal being bounced from your neighbour's meter to your meter to the next. At the end of that line, you could be exposed to possibly 500 or more meters before the information goes to the hub.

Unfortunately, some authorities assume that because smart meter radiation emissions are short in duration and, apparently, lower in power than other everyday wireless devices, they are safe. And many people are unaware of how often these meters communicate. We're told that they transmit SMS-like messages four to six times a day (depending on your service provider), and that may be true for your personal household data – but for mesh networks, the average duty cycle also includes transmissions to maintain the network, sync time and manage network messages (i.e. pass on other houses' data). This can lead to thousands of transmissions per day. Nobody sends that many SMS messages.

In addition, smart meters are never turned off (unlike your mobile phone and wireless router that can be turned off). It's a Chinese water-torture effect, with the continual exposure being more harmful to our bodies. Also, many of these devices are mounted on walls or in wall cavities outside rooms where people spend a significant amount of time, such as the bedroom or lounge room. This means that an incredible stressor on the body is located virtually inside your house.

How do they affect us?

Not surprisingly, live blood-cell analysis has shown that smart meters cause almost immediate damage to the red blood cells of people in their vicinity.[74] The images in Figure 6.2 show what happens to test subjects' blood cells after only two minutes of exposure to a smart meter at a one-foot distance. As you can see, the cells beforehand are perfectly healthy and normal, circular in shape, and not collapsed into another. Afterward, moving from left to right in the image, you can see that cell walls are broken, there are corrugations to the cells' circular shape, and in the last case – cells are coalescing. In the last experiment, the lady had to be pulled away after only 45 seconds because of the severe headaches she was experiencing.

Figure 6.2: The effects of smart meter exposure on cells

Cells before exposure to the smart meter

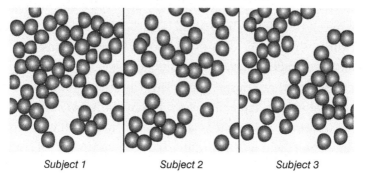

Subject 1   Subject 2   Subject 3

Cells after two minutes of exposure at one foot from the meter

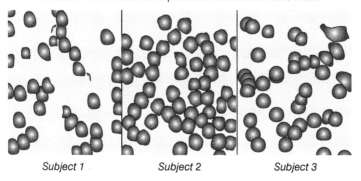

Subject 1   Subject 2   Subject 3

Two other independent studies on symptoms relating to smart meters, conducted on opposite sides of the world, in Australia and the US, had almost identical results, as shown in Figure 6.3. You'll notice that the symptoms listed are consistent with those reported from other wireless devices: insomnia, headaches, ringing in the ears, fatigue, and so on. The one difference was lower levels of stress in the Australian case studies, which could perhaps be explained by Australians' laid-back 'she'll be right mate' attitude to life.

Figure 6.3: Survey results of smart meter symptoms in Australia and the USA[75]

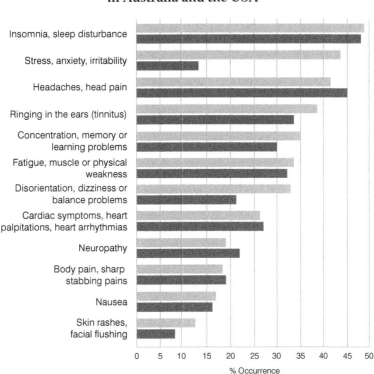

% Occurrence

◼ USA Study   ◼ AUS Case Series

Now, smart meters are installed, or about to be installed, in almost every home! Think about it. A friend of mine recently told me that, as she lives in a block of seven units, she has seven smart meters outside her living room. She was the unlucky one with the owners corporation's electrical box outside her apartment.

Too risky to insure

So, you know how serious it is? For the past two decades, major insurance underwriters Lloyd's of London and Swiss Re, have refused to cover industry for health damages from smart meters, mobile phones and other wireless devices. Similarly, Zurich Financial Services excludes liability related to EMFs under its general insurance policy for corporate liability:

5.8 Electromagnetic fields

any liability of whatsoever nature directly or indirectly caused by, in connection with or contributed to by, or arising from electromagnetic fields (EMF) or electromagnetic interference (EMI).[76]

That means the risk associated with EMFs is too high to insure profitably.

The good news is, there are ways to minimise your exposure to smart meters, including opting out of smart-meter installation – though some states will fight you on this. We'll look at these solutions in more detail in Part 3.

SEVEN

Debating while you suffer

'Delay is the deadliest form of denial.'

—*C. Northcote Parkinson*

L ET'S imagine for a moment that you're hanging off a cliff. Luckily, two of your friends notice this – what a relief! You expect them to come running over, each grab one of your arms and pull you up. But imagine that as they approach, they start arguing about the best way to get you back to safety. Your muscles are aching, your palms are sweaty and you're losing your grip. You scream, 'Just get me up already!' No response. Your friends continuing arguing and saying that the other's proposals are preposterous. How frustrating!

Why aren't we in the know about harmful EMFs? Why isn't the mainstream media getting this information to us? Why isn't there more media dialogue around the issue? Well, the biggest problem has been that authorities have insisted that harmful EMFs can only cause thermal effects – and that there is no biological mechanism by which EMF exposure could affect and damage the body. However, as discussed in Chapter 4, Dr Pall has now demonstrated the biological pathway: the voltage gated calcium channels. And we know that many modern diseases, like ALS, Parkinson's and Alzheimer's, are linked to excessive calcium in the cells.

Proving causality is another problem – almost nothing is totally causal except for a mathematical equation. However, something can be sufficiently co-related, in the absence of any other key contributors to the cause, and a causal relationship can be agreed upon and established. For example, if someone could somehow hold their breath and cause their own death, you might say that 99 per cent of the cause was oxygen deprivation, and the other 1 per cent was the person's stupidity. Because oxygen deprivation was mostly responsible, it would then be sufficient to conclude that this was the cause of death.

The problem with experiments

There are some scientists who know that you can design and experiment in this area to produce any sort of effect you want.

—*Dr Jerry Philips*

Another problem is that experiments into the effects of EMFs are complex to set up for the following reasons:

• **There's a lack of consistency between testing methodologies.** There is no agreed standard method for testing.

- **Many different frequencies affect the testing methods**, when we are focusing on the impact, specifically, across the microwave and radio wave part of the electromagnetic spectrum.

- **Laboratory tests are typically done under artificial lighting,** which we now know places stress on subjects, deregulating normal bodily processes in plants, animals and human beings.

- **Different countries use different technologies, strengths and exposure standards.** Some countries use CDMA, GMA or both technologies for mobile phones; the UK and Australia have power frequencies of 50 Hz while the USA uses 60 Hz. Think about it this way: what if someone told you hot water was anything about 60°C and someone else said it was anything above 55°C? The conclusions of experiments under different exposure standards can be deceiving.

Unfortunately, almost any scientist can tweak their experimental set-up to serve their agenda. You could argue against all the research I've presented, citing equally compelling research suggesting that EMFs are not harmful! For example, one Australian study of mice exposed to mobile phone radiation reported a significant increase in the incidence of cancer of the blood in the mice.[77] A few years later, another group replicated the study but found no significant difference between the exposed mice and the control group. Findings disproven! Or are they? On closer examination, you would discover that the mice in the first study were not handled by scientists, whereas in the second study they were. And it's well known that handling mice causes stress that contributes to disease – so this could explain why *both* groups of mice in the second study had increased incidences of cancer.

Creative manipulation of experiments has generally led to a stalemate on the EMF issue. Consequently, no action has been taken on a global scale.

Slanted science

I've tried to avoid bias when researching the effects of EMFs. When I was writing this chapter, I initially set out to give as much weight to the evidence provided by industry and government experts as I did to the conflicting evidence from more independent scientists that EMFs could be harmful. However, the lack of transparency and amount of junk science from industry and government was such that I felt a balanced approach could not be justified.

When I dug deep into EMF research, a pattern began to appear that I'd seen before in my career as an environmental health professional with issues like lead poisoning, organochlorine pesticides and asbestos. It was similar to the way that scientific literature was skewed and scientific uncertainty manufactured in the debate on tobacco's harmfulness, to influence policy decisions and keep the public confused.

Having said that, don't just blindly believe me: do your own research and decide for yourself. I recommend you read Chapter 8, 'The business of EMF science' in Martin Blank's book *Overpowered*.

Motorola

To explain this pattern, let's look again at the case of Dr Henry Lai, who I mentioned in Chapter 4. Over 20 years ago, Dr Lai and Dr Narendra Singh demonstrated that harmful EMFs damaged DNA, and their work has been repeatedly validated in multiple peer-reviewed studies. But this news was not well accepted by the industry and attempts were made to discredit, defund and fire Dr Lai.

An internal memo leaked from inside Motorola (at the time the world's second-biggest mobile phone manufacturer) and published in *Microwave News* stated that Motorola executives believed they had 'sufficiently war-gamed' Lai and his study. Great science is attacked if it's not consistent with the agenda of the establishment – that's the first part of the pattern.

But to effectively win a war, you must attack from both sides. So Motorola approached a scientist named Dr Jerry Phillips, who had been conducting quality research for years, to 'put a spin on the study' that would be more favourable to the company's interests.[78] Dr Phillips declined, but did complete his own study for Motorola. Everything was friendly until Motorola started to see data they didn't like. Dr Phillips refused to change the language of his work – so Motorola, as owner of the study, changed it for him before publication without his knowledge.[79]

The third piece of the pattern is to muzzle researchers and delay unfavourable results being made public by funding more and more research. Motorola pushed for Phillips to continue his study, offering him more funding to produce more data to delay publishing. Phillips declined:

> I said no. The study's done. I've been doing research for over 25 years. I know when a study is done. I'm going to go ahead and publish the work.[80]

This proved to be the end of his funding from Motorola and coincidently also from the US Department of Energy. Dr Phillips now heads up the Excel Science Center at the University of

Colorado and is one of the endorsers of the report, 'Cellphones and Brain Tumors: 15 reasons for concern – science, spin and the truth behind Interphone', an analysis of the design flaws of the industry-funded Interphone study.[81]

The Interphone study

The large-scale Interphone study is regularly quoted by those who feel EMF is harmless to humanity and the planet. Interphone was created by the International Agency for Research on Cancer (IARC), a division of the World Health Organization, and the research was conducted by 24 separate research organisations across 13 countries. The study found no increase in brain cancer among subjects using mobile phones – and most confusingly, found that a mobile phone actually protects users from brain cancer! What the?

There's much debate surrounding the study's design, funding and lack of transparency. It's beyond the scope of this book to go into detail about it, but I'd recommend reading Dr Phillips' report 'Cellphones and Brain Tumors: 15 reasons for concern' and Chapter 9 of Martin Blank's book *Overpowered*. Both feel that the conclusions reached by the study are almost entirely devoid of scientific merit.

Industry-funded versus non-industry-funded studies

Corporations, private industry and the trade associations that represent them have funded a large proportion of the studies on the effects of EMFs. These days it's very difficult to get funding that doesn't come with some conditions attached – and it's almost impossible to get government research grants if your experiments conflict with government policy.

Dr Lai examined the results of his database of hundreds of studies on EMFs and split them into two piles. One pile was funded by industry and the other stack was independently funded. This is what he found, as illustrated in Figure 7.1 below: 68% of industry studies found that EMFs had no effect, while 70% of independently funded studies found that they had a harmful effect.

Figure 7.1: Conflicting studies into EMF harmful effects – and their finding

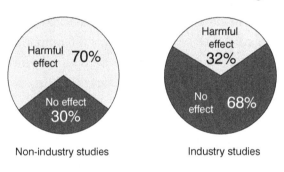

Non-industry studies   Industry studies

Data compiled by Dr Hentry Lai, University of Washington

There's a striking difference. Suspicious, isn't it? Sadly, it's quite common for companies to look at people as numbers on a spreadsheet, and make decisions from there, when life is valuable. Life is precious.

Dr Andrew Marino and the Daubert standard

In the early 1970s, as a result of his research on the biological role of internal electricity, Dr Robert O. Becker warned in *Technology Review* that electromagnetic pollution was real and widespread. He and his colleague Dr Andrew Marino, PhD, JD (a now-retired professor of the departments of Neurology, Orthopedic Surgery and Anatomy and Cellular Biology at Louisiana State University School of Medicine in Shreveport) were invited to testify in a New York State hearing on the safety of high-voltage overhead power lines. The evidence they presented opened the debate about EMFs and health that has raged ever since. Dr Marino found that EMFs cause changes in brain waves, which can ultimately affect the immune system and lead to a variety of diseases.

Investigations into the health of people living near mobile telephone bases show a clear association between a person's distance from an antenna and symptom prevalence. As you can see from Figure 7.2 of a French study,[82] the number of people suffering from typical EMF symptoms decreases the further away from the telecommunication base stations they live.

Figure 7.2 Investigations into the health of people living near mobile telephone relay stations; incidence according to distance and sex

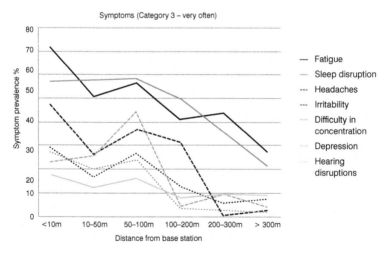

Source: Santini R. et al. 2002

Note: A number of studies provide clear evidence of an association between distance from an antenna and symptom prevalence. This would be not expected if EMR was not the cause.

If you live in Australia, by the way, you can find out how close you live to a base station by visiting www.oztowers.com/Home/Query and typing in your postcode. This study suggests that it would be a good idea to live at least 300 metres away.

Back to Andrew Marino's story. Dr Marino worked with Dr Becker and fought many corporations (power companies, mostly) in court over their installation of power lines close to residential homes, and their effects on citizens' lives. To cut a long story short, it turns out that in a court of law, you can't argue on the basis of whether scientific studies are valid or invalid in their conclusions. Instead, the opinions of well-paid experts in medicine and science are accepted as fact.

This means that big corporations with big wallets can pay a panel of 20 experts and have them testify in support of their case, and their opinion will not be heavily questioned. Needless to say, this does not educate the jury and allow them to decide for themselves who's innocent or guilty.

Dr Marino's 40-year long journey as a scientist, and eventually a lawyer, led to him bringing to light the Daubert standard, and pushing to make sure it was used in all environmental science proceedings. The standard is a rule of evidence on whether the testimony of expert witnesses is admissable in United States federal legal proceedings.

The Daubert standard educates and enables lawyers to interrogate experts about how they know what they claim to be true. It's a game-changer – it means that the validity of the experts' claims can be assessed. If you want to find out more, you absolutely must read Dr Marino's book *Going Somewhere: truth about a life in science.* The future is hopeful if brave lawyers choose to read this book, educate themselves on environmental health and use Daubert in court hearings and cross-examinations.

Just like me, Dr Marino believes that science must be socially just, serving the people. He believes that, without a doubt, the phone and power companies will pay for their crimes to humanity in exposing us to EMFs. My take is more moderate: they'll learn, and with the weight of public displeasure upon them, adjust their business strategies to take human well-being into consideration – in order to satisfy their commercial interests in the long run. Never underestimate the power of the people. With social connectivity these days, the consumer has the power to dictate the destiny of the market and hence what businesses do. Step into that!

EIGHT

Signs of change

'Many a revolution started with the actions of a few.'

—Wynton Marsalis

W E maybe on the cusp of a transition on the issue of harmful EMFs, although I'm not holding my breath. On 22 May 2016, the US National Toxicology Program (NTP) made a public announcement that mobile phone radiation presents a cancer risk for humans. The NTP radiation project, which has been underway for over 10 years, is the program's most expensive undertaking, costing more than $25 million so far.[83] It has found statistically *significant* cancer rates among rats exposed to mobile phone signals for two years, contradicting the conventional wisdom of most doctors, biologists, physicists, epidemiologists, engineers, journalists and so on. Ron Melnick, who led the team, sums up the program's findings:

The NTP tested the hypothesis that cell phone radiation could not cause health effects and that hypothesis has now been disproved... The experiment has been done and, after extensive reviews, the consensus is that there was a carcinogenic effect.

What governments decide to do with these results is unknown, but at least the science is becoming clearer and clearer. Governments are in a double bind, having mandated the rollout of smart meters to link up to a smart grid to allow for a wireless communication system to operate smart cities. But here is the government's dilemma, 'smart cities' cannot function without the use of harmful EMF signals.

New legislation

Europe and the UK are leading the way in protecting people from harmful EMFs. On 29 June 2013, the European Union issued the Electromagnetic Fields Directive and gave member states three years to implement it as law. In the UK, despite Brexit, it is not expected that the UK parliament will hold off from enacting *The Control of Electromagnetic Fields at Work Regulations 2016* (CEFAW). The risk of EMFs has previously been managed through existing legislation – mainly the *Health and Safety at Work Act* and the *Management of Health and Safety at Work Regulations* – but the Electromagnetic Fields Directive introduces new responsibilities for employers, most notably a requirement to assess the levels of EMFs to which their workers may be exposed against a set of specific thresholds.[84] The CEFAW regulations also require employers to:

- ensure that exposure is below a set of exposure limit values (ELVs)

- when appropriate, devise and implement an action plan to ensure compliance with the exposure limits
- when appropriate, assess the risks of employees' exposure and eliminate or minimise those risks – workers at particular risk, such as expectant mothers and those with active or passive implanted or body-worn medical devices, must be taken into account
- provide information and training on the particular risks, if any, posed to employees by EMFs in the workplace and give details of any action taken to remove or control them
- take action if employees are exposed to EMFs in excess of the ELVs
- provide health surveillance as appropriate.

It's a long way from protecting the general public, but it's an encouraging sign nonetheless.

Insurance

I mentioned in Chapter 6 that insurer Lloyd's of London excluded any liability coverage for injuries from some wireless devices (e.g. smart meters) in 2015. Lloyd's has also acknowledged that if EMFs are proven to cause cancer, long latency periods may be obscuring the evidence at present. The company has drawn a comparison with the development of asbestos compensation, warning that 'a small number of legal cases can change the situation very rapidly', and the insurance industry would likely be under-reserved if EMF did emerge as a compensable injury under product and employers' liability policies.[85] They clarified:

The Electromagnetic Fields Exclusion (Exclusion 32) is a General Insurance Exclusion and is applied across the market as standard. The purpose of the exclusion is to exclude cover for illnesses caused by continuous long-term non-ionizing radiation exposure.

In 2014, global reinsurer Swiss Re rated electromagnetic fields as one of the six top risks businesses face – 'Risk from dangers linked to EMF can be classified as an emergent risk.' 'Emergent risk' is the category that was once occupied by asbestos. What do you know!

For underwriters servicing the Australian insurance market, EMFs are not a standard exclusion in policy wording, but is considered on a case-by-case basis if raised by the broker.

Financial compensation for EHS

In 2013 in Australia, CSIRO worker Dr Alexander McDonald was awarded financial compensation for having been made disabled by wireless signal tests. The Administrative Appeals Tribunal of Australia approved the workers compensation due to electro-magnetic hypersensitivity (EHS), even though EHS is not recognised here as a medical condition. This is a good sign, and provides a precedent for future court proceedings by those who experience acute symptoms associated with EMF.

Industry begins to take action

Australia's largest mobile phone network provider, Telstra, sent the following text message out several times to all users. As with Apple's guidelines about radio wave exposure in their legal fine print, consider it a warning!

A service message from Telstra.
For information on mobile use,
Electromagnetic Energy and tips
to reduce exposure, visit http://
telstra.com.au/mobiletips

But what I find most inspiring is how industry is beginning to make bold moves to decrease electromagnetic interference. Apple is applying EMI (Electro Magnetic Interference) Shield technology to a variety of digital chips – radio frequency and connectivity (wireless local area networks [WLAN], Bluetooth) chips and others. The added benefit is that this reduces electromagnetic interference that can affect the functionality of their devices. The function of technology and the well-being of humans can overlap, and should. This is the sort of innovation I think we all need to promote.

Inventors are seeing opportunities to patent new ideas, too. A Swiss patent (WO 2004/075583 2) uses an automated sleep mode method and system to reduce harmful EMFs generated by WLANs. The invention has the potential to greatly reduce harmful EMFs from WLANs during times when there is low or no network activity.

Humanity is waking up to the issue, and that includes business. But it's taking a while – government wheels turn slowly and big corporates will not compromise profits unless forced. In the meantime, you and I need fast solutions that work. We'll look at this in Part 3, where I'll share some of the new ways to avoid the harmful effects of living in a technologically connected world.

Part summary

- **EMFs generated by modern technology are stressors to the body**, especially radio waves and microwaves, which power a lot of today's technologies. The stress they apply can lead to numerous chronic diseases. Even if you feel healthy now, the effects may take time to reveal themselves. And you don't want to sit around for years to find out for sure!

- **The problem is here to stay**, so we must apply smart thinking and solutions to address it now, and into the future.

- **People who are a part of the justice system should read Andrew Marino's book *Going Somewhere* and educate themselves on the Daubert standard.** This will prime them to cross-examine scientists appropriately, rather than take experts' claims on face value. Remember, scientific experiment, oxymoronically, is quite an art, and experiments can be rigged to skew results.

- **Governments are stalling due to the double bind they're in.** While there are signs of change, it isn't moving fast enough, certainly considering the pace at which technologies are becoming integrated into the fabric of our lives.

---

35 Dr Robert Becker (1923–2008) was a man far, far ahead of his time, producing five decades of electro-medical research. In the 1960s, he warned that power frequency and radio wave fields were damaging to human health. After a controversial *60 Minutes* interview, he lost his research funding and was forced out of the Veterans Administration Hospital in Syracuse University (www.solamarsolution.com/uncategorized/interview-of-dr-robert-o-becker-by-dan-rather-on-cbs-60-minutes-13-february-1977). In my view, he deserved a Nobel Prize in Medicine.

36 The Schumann resonances (SR) are a set of spectrum peaks in the extremely low frequency (ELF) portion of the earth's electromagnetic field spectrum. Schumann

resonances are global electromagnetic resonances, generated and excited by lightning discharges in the cavity formed by the earth's surface and the ionosphere, <https://en.wikipedia.org/wiki/Schumann_resonances>

37 Dr Magda Havas, PHD, *The Disease of 'Modern' Civilization . . . Neurasthenia*, <www.magdahavas.com/the-disease-of-modern-civilization-neurasthenia/>

38 Jack Kruse, 2013, *EMF 5: What are the Biologic Effects of EMF?* <https://www.jackkruse.com/emf-5-what-are-the-biologic-effects-of-emf/>

39 Opening Pandora's Box, 1984, BBC Special Channel 4, producer David Jones, Fulcrum Central Productions, <http://mindjustice.org/BBCposta2012.htm> for full transcript video: https://vimeo.com/101427389

40 Voltairenet.org, *What spooked the USS Donald Cook so much in the Black Sea?* <http://www.voltairenet.org/article185860.html>

41 Kjell Hansson Mild, Mike Repacholi, Emilie van Deventer, Paolo Ravazzani, 2004, *Electromagnetic Hypersensitivity*, International Workshop on EMF Hypersensitivity Proceedings, Czech Republic, http://www.who.int/peh-emf/publications/reports/EHS_Proceedings_June2006.pdf?ua=1

42 www.electromagneticman.co.uk

43 www.betweenrockandhardplace.wordpress.com/2014/10/18/former-nokia-technology-chief-mobile-phones-wrecked-my-health/

44 https://docs.google.com/file/d/0B1KQ639Tc1Z9WTl4RG5oSjRRS0k/edit?pli=1

45 www.emfanalysis.com/about

46 www.wddty.com/magazine/2014/april/electrosensitivity.html

47 www.beyondthevan.com/about-us

48 www.eligiblemagazine.com/2016/06/26/wi-fi-fatal-attraction/

49 www.dailymail.co.uk/health/article-1195551/It-happened--Im-allergic-modern-life.html

50 Dr Magda Havas, 2012, March 2012 *Guideline of the Austrian Medical Association for Diagnosing and Treating Patients of EMF Related Health Problems and Illnesses (EMF Syndrome) with Electrohypersensitivity.*

51 Örjan Hallberg and Gerd Oberfeld, 2006, *Letter to the editor: will we all become electrosensitive?* Electromagn Biol Med, p.189-91.

52 Apple website, iPhone 6 RF Exposure Information, <http://www.apple.com/legal/rfexposure/iphone7,2/en/>

53 Martha R. Herbert with Karen Weintraub, 2012, *The Autism Revolution: Whole Body Strategies for Making Life All It Can Be*, Ballantine/Harvard Health Publications.

54 Herbert, Martha R., and Cindy Sage, 2013, *Autism and EMF? Plausibility of a pathophysiological link–Part I*, Pathophysiology 20.3: 191-209 and Part II: 211-234.

55 Jack Kruse, 2013, *What Are the Biologic Effects of EMF?* <https://www.jackkruse.com/emf-5-what-are-the-biologic-effects-of-emf/>

56 Pall, M. L., 2013, *Electromagnetic fields act via activation of voltage-gated calcium channels to produce beneficial or adverse effects,* Journal of Cellular and Molecular Medicine, Vol. 17, Issue 8, pages 958–965.

57 Dr Magda Havas, PHD, Biography, <http://www.magdahavas.com/biography/>

58 Richard Lear, 2016, *Root Cause in the Dramatic Rise of Chronic Disease*, <http://mieuxprevenir.blogspot.com.au/2016/05/root-cause-in-dramatic-rise-of-chronic.html>

59 Pacher P, Beckman JS, Liaudet L, 2007, *Nitric oxide and peroxynitrite in health and disease*, Physiology Reviews.

60 Henry Lai, 2012, *Genetic Effects of Non-Ionizing Electromagnetic Fields*, Section 6 BioInitiative Report.

61 Brian Stein and Alasdair Phillips, 2011, *The Evidence Connecting Mobile Phone EMF Exposure and Male Infertility*.

62 V.M. Burugh and L.I. Lipshulz, 2004, *Male Factor Infertility: Evaluations and Management*, Medical Clinics of North America 88, No. 2, p. 367-385.

63 S. La Vignera et al., 2011, *Effects of the Exposure to Mobile Phones on Male Reproduction: A Review of the Literature*, Journal of Andrology 33, No. 3, p. 350-356.

64 Ariel Zilberlich et al, 2015, *Habits of cell phone usage and sperm quality – does it warrant attention?* Reproductive BioMedicine, Vol. 31, Issue 3, p. 421-426.

65 Christopher J. Portier, Wendy L. Leonard, 2016, *Do Cellphones Cause Cancer? Probably, but it's Complicated*, Scientific American Blog.

66 Joel Moskowitz, 2010, *Government Must Inform US of Cell Phone Risk*, San Francisco Chronicle.

67 Chapman S, Azizi L, Luo Q, Sitas F, 2016, *Has the incidence of brain cancer risen in Australia since the introduction of mobile phones 29 years ago?* Cancer Epidemiology.

68 *Enough Rope*, ABC TV, 2008.

69 Environmental Health Trust, *NIH National Toxicology Program Cell Phone Radiofrequency Radiation Study*, <www.ehtrust.org/cell-phone-radiofrequency-radiation-study/>

70 C. K. Chou, et al, 1992, *Long-Term, Low-Level Microwave Irradiation of Rats*, Bioelectromagnetics 13, p. 469-496.

71 Dr. George Carlo and Martin Schram, 2001, *Cell Phones, Invisible Hazards in the Wireless Age, An Insiders Alarming Discoveries About Cancer and Genetic Damage*, Carroll & Graf Publishers, New York.

72 Lennart Hardell, 2014, *Moving radiofrequency radiation from Group 2B to 1 as a human carcinogen*, https://lennarthardellenglish.wordpress.com/2014/12/08/moving-radiofrequency-radiation-from-group-2b-to-1-as-a-human-carcinogen/

73 http://www.itu.int/en/ITU-D/Statistics/Pages/stat/default.aspx.

74 Lloyd Burrell, 2013, *Smart Meter Radiation – Live Blood Analysis*, Electric Sense, <www.electricsense.com/6665/smart-meter-radiation-live-blood-analysis/>

75 Helteman, PhD., statistics, final results Summary: Wireless Utility Meter Safety Impacts Survey, September 13, 2011, p. 22 (http://emfsafetynetwork.org/wp-content/uploads/2011/09/Wireless-Utility-Meter-Safety-Impacts-Survey-Results-Final.pdf). 97 per cent of respondents to full survey were in the USA, from 28 states with most in California (78 per cent) and New York (16 per cent). (318 individuals). Federica Lamech, MBBS, Self-Reporting of Symptom Development from Exposure to Radiofrequency Fields of Wireless Smart Meters in Victoria, Australia: A Case Series. Alternative Therapies. Nov/Dec 2014, Vol. 20, No. 6, pages 28-38. NIH PMID 25478801 (92 individuals)

76 Zurich Combined General Liability Insurance, https://www.zurich.com.au/content/dam/australia/general_insurance/corporate_lia bility/combined_general_liability_insurance_policy.pdf

77 Repacholi et al., 1997, *Lymphomus in Eu-pim 1 transgenic mic exposed to pulsed 900MHz electromagnetic fields*, Radiation Res. 147, p. 631-640.

78 Melinda Wenner, 2012, *Cellphone Games*, The Walrus, <http://thewalrus.ca/cellphone-games/>

79 'Mobile Phone Health Risks,' transcript of BBC television show Panorama interview with reporter Paul Kenyon and Dr George Carlo, May 5, 1999.

80 http://lavida.kgnu.net/lavidaradioshow.php?show_id=269

81 Radiation Research, 2009, *Cellphones and Brain Tumors: 15 Reasons for Concern – Science, Spin and the Truth Behind Interphone*, <http://www.radiationresearch.org/pdfs/reasons_us.pdf>

82 Santini R, et al, 2002, *Investigation on the health of people living near mobile telephone relay stations: Incidence according to distance and sex*. Pathology Biology, Paris.

83 Microwave News, 2016, *Cell Phone Radiation Boosts Cancer Rates in Animals; $25 Million NTP Study Finds Brain Tumors U.S. Government Expected To Advise Public of Health Risk*, <http://microwavenews.com/news-center/ntp-cancer-results>

84 SHP Online, 2016, *Explained: CEFAW Regulations, which come into force today*, <http://www.shponline.co.uk/explained-cefaw-regulations-which-come-into-force-today/>

85 Lloyd's of London, 2010, *Electro-Magnetic Fields from Mobile Phones: Recent Developments*.

PART THREE

WHAT YOU CAN DO

'Every great and deep difficulty bears in itself
its own solution. It forces us to change our
thinking in order to find it.'

—*Niels Bohr*

NINE

A breath of fresh light

'The problem is not to find the answer, it's to face the answer.'

—*Terence McKenna*

EVERYONE lives life differently, so everyone has different levels of exposure to harmful EMFs and artificial light, and different degrees of shielding from natural sunlight. So how do you address this? What are the solutions? Well, one option, of course, is to live far out in the bush like our healthy friend in earlier chapters – in sync with the natural environment, with access to full-spectrum sunlight (photons) and grounded to the earth (gaining electrons) from working barefoot daily in your organic garden. You wake with the morning sun and retire not long after sunset, have minimal exposure to artificial lighting, and there's no wi-fi or mobile phone reception.

It would be a super-healthy living environment, although there are still several sneaky traps to be aware of, including EMFs emitted by the transformers in your solar panels, wind turbines and back-up generators. Let's get real, though. Many of us are too committed to our careers, our children's schools and our extended family to move. Just try telling your boss, 'I refuse to work in the office. It's not good for my health.' Good luck with that! Nor is it easy to live in this day and age without ever looking at a computer or TV screen.

Many of us love living in a vibrant city with access to great theatres, restaurants and sporting venues. I know I do! We love the many new choices and conveniences that advances in technology have afforded us, too. The internet allows us to check the weather, get directions, shop, connect, find out where the person we're meeting is, record precious memories, and so much more.

Of course, if you're fortunate enough to find your idyllic cabin in the country and you never want to explore the outside world again – go for it! I wish you the best. But likely this isn't you. Likely, it's not anyone you know.

If you live in the city, particularly the inner city, you're bombarded by both artificial lights and intense EMFs. So ask yourself, when (if at all!) do you get natural sunlight and time away from modern technology? In the half-hour you spend reading a book (not an ebook!) at lunchtime? During early-morning walks with the dog? Or perhaps it's on the weekend, where you get outside and switch off? Give this some consideration, as understanding your environment really matters when you're choosing solutions to help you avoid the harmful effects of an increasingly technology-reliant world.

The more disconnected from nature and addicted to technology and modern life you are, the more effort you need to put into minimising your exposure to harmful EMFs and artificial light. As Dr Jack Kruse keeps reminding the members of his forum, 'You can't get well by staying in the same environment that made you sick in the first place'. One day, your postcode may well be considered more important to your health and well-being than your DNA, and suburbs with densely populated high-rise buildings may become a new category of contaminated site, deluged with blue light and harmful EMFs from things like wireless smart devices, electric autonomous vehicles and the 'internet of everything'.

If you love to travel – did you know when you fly, you're treating yourself like a steak in the microwave? You heat up and dry out as radiation bounces around dehydrating your cells and producing inflammation. Now, I'm a lifetime Qantas Gold frequent flyer, and I love to travel! As Australians we live, as former Prime Minister Paul Keating once said, at 'the arse end of the world', and it can make one yearn for what's going on in the Northern Hemisphere. However, today most planes have or will soon have wi-fi. Qantas CEO Alan Joyce has you covered:

> You won't be limited to checking your email or Facebook – it's going to be about watching the football live, streaming your favourite TV show or movie, catching up on the latest YouTube videos, or shopping online.

That's 400 passengers streaming wireless signals buzzing around in what's basically a Faraday cage – that is, the metal shell of the plane acts to help keep the signals inside. Add to that magnetic fields from the plane's engines and cosmic radiation, and it looks like travellers are cooked! Us 'arse-enders' forced to suffer 24-hour flights to Europe will arrive well done.

The good news is, there are measures you can take and exciting new technologies you can use that will allow you to live in your favourite city, have your modern lifestyle and all the digital toys you love.

In the rest of Part 3 of this book, I'm going to:

- explain the hierarchy of controls and how you can apply these to minimise your exposure to artificial light and manmade EMFs (Chapter 10)
- walk you through some solutions for the typical modern family lifestyle (Chapter 11)
- introduce the breakthrough technological solutions available – which will continue to evolve in the coming years (Chapter 12)
- tell you what I do to protect myself (Chapter 13).

Not all the solutions are easy or hassle-free, but many are fairly convenient and conducive to a modern lifestyle. The choice, as always, is yours as to how much effort and cash you want to invest in your health and your family's.

TEN

The hierarchy of controls

'A problem well-defined is a problem half solved.'

—John Dewey

A LLOW me to introduce a very well-known industry standard or managing hazards. The hierarchy of controls is a standard approach to safety in the workplace and is taught in work health and safety courses. I believe it to also be a useful tool for considering ways to manage the risks posed by our addiction to technology and modern indoor life, in particular the effects of artificial light, lack of full-spectrum sunlight and manmade EMFs.

Take a look at Figure 10.1 overleaf, which summarises the hierarchy. You can see that the controls are placed in order from most effective to least effective, but for our purposes, I wouldn't worry too much about that. 'Most and least effective' is intended to factor in the probability of human error when operating machinery and so on – our hazards are environmental, not occupational, so all stages can provide effective control if they're implemented properly.

Figure 10.1: Hierarchy of Controls

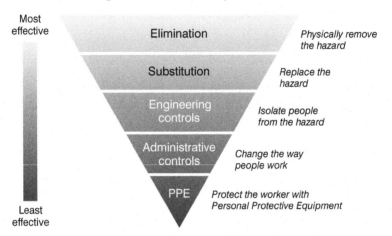

Stage 1 – Elimination

Elimination is where you physically remove the hazard, getting rid of it altogether. If you've read this far, you should realise that it's virtually impossible to eliminate artificial light and manmade EMFs from your life. You could move to the bush, as we discussed in Chapter 9, or you could try lobbying government and industry to stop producing products and technologies that generate artificial lighting and manmade EMFs – good luck with that!

Stage 2 – Substitution

Substitution is where you replace the hazard with something less hazardous. So for example, to limit artificial lighting at night, you could replace your light bulbs with ones that more closely replicate full-spectrum light, or use candlelight. Similarly, if you have a cordless phone that emits harmful EMFs, you could replace it with a corded phone – one of the old-fashioned ones with curly tails.

Stage 3 – Engineering controls

Engineering controls involve isolating people from the hazard using mechanical aids, barriers or shielding. For example, you could cut off all electricity from your bedroom using an electrical circuit-breaker, while leaving the rest of house connected so the fridge stays cold.

Some EHS sufferers build themselves a Faraday cage to work and sleep in – an earthed metal piece of equipment or room that excludes electrostatic and electromagnetic influences. If you lived in a Faraday cage for the rest of your life, you would eliminate manmade EMFs. You would not, however, be able to use a mobile phone, wi-fi or any other EMF-emitting technology – harmful EMFs generated from devices used inside a Faraday cage keep bouncing around inside the cage with you.

Stage 4 – Administrative controls

Administrative controls involve changing the way people work, establishing policies, procedures and practices to manage the risks. In your own life, this might translate to taking a morning walk at sunrise and exposing your arms and face to low levels of full-spectrum light, switching off artificial lighting after sunset, and turning off your wi-fi and putting your smartphone in aeroplane mode while you sleep. This involves effort, and of course it depends what you're willing to compromise on.

Stage 5 – Personal Protective Equipment

Stage 5 involves protecting people with Personal Protective Equipment or 'PPE', in cases when you can't eliminate, substitute or control the hazard. This is the situation most people are facing now with artificial light and harmful EMFs. Fortunately, using environmental PPE you can effectively nullify the risks. That's why I said earlier not to worry too much about the 'most to least effective' scale on the hierarchy – given that most of us live in cities, these hazards aren't going away, and so PPE is actually a very effective thing to implement.

Assessing your risks

Now, take a look at this list of the common sources of EMFs in your home or office (we're excluding artificial lighting, as that's obvious):

- wi-fi routers
- wireless modems
- wireless video game consoles
- wireless burglar alarms
- wireless baby monitors
- Bluetooth devices
- TV and computer screens
- electrical wiring
- computers and laptops
- wireless printers
- 'smart' appliances
- digital alarm clocks
- smart meters

- microwave ovens
- smartphones and tablets
- cordless phones
- solar panel invertors.

I would be surprised if you didn't have most of these. Now, here are some other hazards you might be exposed to that come from outside your home or office:

- telecommunication tower antennas and base stations
- radio and TV antennas
- electricity substations
- high-voltage cables
- your neighbours' smart meters.

Hazards are pretty much everywhere – and these lists are far from exhaustive. EHS sufferers and those who are serious about identifying all the EMFs they are exposed to will need to hire testing equipment or engage a professional such as a building biologist.

Three types of EMFs, three testing devices

There are three different types of EMF to measure, and three devices for measuring them:

1. **A radio frequency (RF) meter to measure microwave and RF radiation** from, for example, wireless technology and telecommunication towers. I personally consider that exposure to the continuous fields generated by always-on wireless devices poses the biggest environmental threat to humanity today.

2. **A Gauss meter to measure magnetic fields** from power lines, appliances and incorrectly installed home wiring. Magnetic fields are arguably the most dangerous EMF, but are not usually much of an issue unless you live near high-voltage power lines or have an old house with poorly installed wiring. However, with the rollout of the smart grid powered by smart meters and fed by smart devices and appliances electrical wiring in our homes is likely to become very dirty.

3. **A battery-powered AM radio to test for 'dirty electricity'** in your electrical wiring from home appliances, florescent lighting and dimmer switches.

Trifield meters are able to measure all three types of electro-magnetic field: AC magnetic field, AC electric field and radio (including microwaves).

If you suffer from EHS, you may also wish to measure body electrical fields, and I would encourage you to visit websites dedicated to EHS and EMFs to learn more about preventative measures. I recommend www.emfwise.com and Jeromy Johnson's site www.emfanalysis.com.

ELEVEN

An at-risk family – no more

'There is nothing like first-hand evidence.'

—Sherlock Holmes

LET'S walk through how you might implement control measures in a typical modern family setting now. Let's suppose you have a family of four – mum, dad, a teenager and a younger child who has just started school. They live in a house around a 20-minute drive from the city, and their home has wi-fi, a flat-screen television, and lots of LED lighting and modern appliances – some of which have antennas so they can connect wirelessly to the recently installed smart meter. Everyone in the family has a smartphone, laptop or iPad, even the youngest child.

Dad works hard to support his family at a new start-up technology company, spending long hours at the office in front of a computer. He typically starts his day around 6am, leaving home early to beat the morning traffic, and works till at least 7pm. Often he takes work home, and he sleeps with his phone on his bedside table, checking his emails as soon as he rises. He eats well, though, exercises at the gym whenever he can, and tries to get to sleep before midnight.

He's completely disconnected from nature, and not surprisingly, is suffering the symptoms of mild EHS, including headaches, fatigue, weight gain and trouble sleeping. Because he doesn't have a 'serious' illness, however, he continues to live life in this way.

Mum is the concerned hero. She has a science degree and works part-time at a laboratory, while also taking on the lion's share of the domestic tasks. To support the family's well-being, she's picky about what they eat and buys mainly organic foods, and for her own health, she practises yoga. She intuitively knows that her family has become a bit too addicted to technology, regularly asking her teenage daughter to get off her phone and her husband to stop checking emails. In recent times, she's been having trouble focusing, and complains of brain fog.

The couple's adolescent daughter is constantly on her iPhone (mostly using social media), and finds herself struggling to focus on her studies too. And despite getting lots of exercise and playing sport at school, she finds that her emotions and energy levels are erratic and her relationship with her parents is deteriorating. At school, everyone, including the teacher, works on school-provided wireless connected laptops; most classes are taught using presentation software and a projector or smart whiteboards.

The young son has just started Grade 1 and has been diagnosed with mild Attention Deficit Hyperactivity Disorder (ADHD). His teachers think he lacks focus, although he's always very focused when he plays sport out in the park.

Day after day, Mum looks at her family and herself and wonders why they all seem so tired and erratic. How can her son have ADHD when he's so well looked after? Is this normal? Is this what life should be like? Deep inside, she knows it isn't. So she puts on her science hat and starts doing research. At yoga, she talks to a health-conscious friend who suggests that the family's health problems might be diet-related. They carefully go through her shopping list, but no obvious culprit is found. As for exercise, the whole family is sport-oriented and they get more exercise than most. Then another friend joins the conversation and suggests that the family's disconnection from nature may be having an impact. She points out that the family spends most of their time indoors exposed to excessive artificial light and manmade EMFs. At first, Mum finds this idea ridiculous, but she's always eager to learn, so she reads the books and websites her friend recommends.

As a result, she decides to test the house. Her daughter asks to help out with the survey and write the findings up for a school science assignment. They both read up on how to test their house and hire meters that test for both wireless and magnetic EMFs.

They start outside, testing the street's power lines. The meter drops down towards zero as they walk away from the house, but as they approach it and enter the garage, the meter starts screaming. Dumbfounded, they look around, but see nothing obvious. Using the meter, they discover that the signal is coming from a wall with nothing on it – so they go back outside to look at the external wall. They find that the source of the EMFs is the newly installed smart meter.

Then they go through the entire house and backyard. They are shocked at how many other devices they find emitting EMFs –

the wi-fi router; their phones, including the cordless phones; the game console; their computers; the TV; the printer; the alarm clocks; almost all the new appliances; the microwave; the ceiling in the son's upstairs bedroom (which they trace to the solar panels on the roof); and some poor wiring in the old laundry.

The two of them do their best to explain it to Dad; Mum tells him, 'Get back to nature. You need some time off. Having bad health does your company no good, after all. Let's get away from the busy life and technology for a bit – it'll do us all good.' Dad, of course, thinks she's mad – until his daughter turns on the meter in his new Tesla SUV and the meter starts to scream. New cars are full of wireless technology: we no longer drive cars, we drive computers.

The daughter gets a good mark for her assignment, but the teacher comments that she has overstated the health risks, saying, 'The scientific evidence does not establish that exposure to extremely low frequency EMFs found around the home, the office or near power lines and other electrical sources is a hazard to human health.' The teacher is supportive of the school's wireless initiatives and likes teaching using laptops instead of textbooks; she refuses to read the references quoted in the assignment.

So what can the family do? Let's look now at the remedial solutions for some of the biggest sources of harmful EMFs found in the home, using the hierarchy of controls perspective where applicable.

Smart meters

As I've mentioned before, the problem with smart meters is that they're virtually inside your house and are never turned off. These are a real menace to our health. Let's apply the hierarchy of controls.

1. **Elimination.** Eliminating the hazard is almost impossible, unless you move to the bush and live off grid.

2. **Substitution.** Substituting can be a battle, as most states and territories in Australia have mandated the installation of smart meters, if they're not already installed. If you're lucky enough not to have one installed yet, lock your meter box and put signs saying 'No trespassing' and 'Do NOT fit a smart meter' on the outside. If your smart meter is already installed, contact your supplier and asked to opt out; if they refuse, visit stopsmartmeters.com.au for further actions you can take.

3. **Engineering controls.** Smart meters can be covered with an absorbent or reflector shield so that harmful EMFs do not enter your house. This is best done by an expert; the golden rule with shielding is to have an RF meter on hand and take readings before and after the work is done to ensure its effectiveness. Beware of reflections and make sure you don't direct the beam into your neighbour's house. Also try to make sure the beam from their meter doesn't point in your direction. Remember it's always better to shield a device rather than a person.

4. **Administrative controls.** Not applicable.

5. **PPE.** Install a Blushield plug-in device (which we'll discuss in the next chapter) to provide coherent fields that allow you to be invisible to harmful EMFs.

Mobile phones

Guess where I found the best collection of tips for reducing your exposure to mobile phone radiation? In a phone retailer's blog, of course! Always go to the source. The steps that Verizon retailer TCC recommends you take can be read on the tccrocks.com website.[86] We have paraphrased them for you below.

- **Don't hold your phone close to your body when you are using it.** Even a small amount of space between you and your phone reduces markedly the amount of radiation you absorb. Likewise, don't keep your phone in your pocket or clipped to your belt.

- **Use your mobile phone for emergencies and important calls only.** When your mobile is turned on it is intermittently emitting radiation, even if you're not making a call. Pregnant women in particular should follow this advice.

- **Learn about the potential effects of radiation on reproductive health.** Don't keep your mobile phone near your genitals. Cell phone radiation damages sperm in males and there is some evidence of reproductive health effects. There is also preliminary evidence of increased breast cancer risk for women who kept cell phones in their bras.

- **Avoid using your phone when the signal is weak.** The weaker the signal, the more the radio frequency has to boost itself to get connected, increasing your exposure.

- **Turn your mobile off at night or place it away from your head when you are sleeping.** This will protect your immune system and your mental health. Also turn off all routers in the house before bed.

- **Point your mobile phone away from you.** If you have to carry your phone, position the keyboard part toward your body and the back toward the outside to have the electromagnetic fields move away from you.

- **Don't assume some phones are less harmful than others.** Industry promoted SAR ratings are virtually useless in measuring the true potential biological danger as almost all of the damage is not done by heat transfer, which SAR measures.

- **Read the fine print in your phone.** Cell phone companies give specific instructions and guidelines on phone use.

- **Don't use your phone in closed-in metal areas, such as in lifts, cars, trains or planes.** Mobile phones draw more power, and emit more radiation, in enclosed metal spaces.

- **Don't wear metal-rimmed glasses when using a mobile phone.**

- **Switch your mobile to flight mode when it is not in use.** Flight mode turns off the wireless transmitter thereby reducing exposure to radiation fields.

If you, like me, must use your mobile phone more often than you care to admit, use speaker mode. Wired headsets are not a good solution, as there is some concern that they may function as an antenna, increasing harmful EMF exposure to your head. I prefer to use 'air tube' headsets, as there's some evidence that using air rather than using a metal wire to channel sound vibrations provides a level of protection.

The Night Shift feature in Apple devices

At the time of writing, Apple's latest operating system for its devices has a mode called 'Night Shift', which aims both to reduce eye strain when viewing the device in the dark and reduce the amount of blue light emitted, which has an adverse impact on people's circadian rhythms. In Apple's words:

> Many studies have shown that exposure to bright blue light in the evening can affect your circadian rhythms and make it harder to fall asleep. Night Shift uses your iOS device's clock and geolocation to determine when it's sunset in your location. Then it automatically shifts the colors in your display to the warmer end of the spectrum, making it easier on your eyes. In the morning, it returns the display to its regular settings.

Cordless phones

Digital cordless phones such as DECT phones can be even more of a problem than mobile phones, due to their 24/7 wireless radiation while plugged in. Here are some solutions:

1. **Elimination.** Throw away your cordless phone and don't talk to anyone unless they visit in person. Not a great solution, is it?

2. **Substitution.** Replace the cordless phone with a corded one, or a low-radiation DECT cordless phone. Or use Skype (with a phone number), with a wired external microphone and hard wired computer.

3. **Engineering controls.** Unplug your cordless phone at night (that's to say remove the plug from the electric socket on the wall) and remove the handsets from areas where you spend

time – even unplugged, charged handsets can still emit EMFs (handset seeking to connect with the base) until the battery has run down. Put the base of your cordless phone at least two metres away from where you spend any significant amount of time (remember EMFs travel through walls). Have at least one corded phone in your home, so if you do disconnect your cordless phones you've still got a phone to use.

4. **Administrative controls.** Plug the cordless phone in only when you use it. You might need to plug it in an hour or two before use to charge it, but once charged, most DECT phones have four or five days' battery life. Also, keep your conversations short and use the speakerphone function when you can, to keep the phone away from your head as much as possible.

5. **PPE.** Install a Blushield plug-in device.

Wi-fi devices, routers, modems and Bluetooth devices

This category includes TVs, laptops, desktop computers, smartphones, tablets, game consoles and any other gadget that wirelessly connects to the internet. Typically, these are some of the biggest contributors of harmful EMFs inside your house. The solutions:

1. **Elimination.** Not possible, unless you decide to join an Amish community. However, you can move wireless devices as far away from you as possible, and especially away from bedrooms.

2. **Substitution.** Swap to a wired router.

3. **Engineering controls.** Hardwire all devices, including computers, TVs game consoles and controllers, printers, keyboards, mice, speakers and so on. Beware of 'standby mode' – some devices such as game consoles will keep looking for a wireless controller to turn them on unless you turn them off at the power point. Even iPads and smart phones can also be hardwired, type 'hardwire an iPad' into YouTube for instructions.

4. **Administrative controls.** Turn off the wi-fi router at bedtime. You can set an automatic power timer to make this easy; some companies even allow you to manage the wireless settings online. Note that some routers can continue to emit EMFs even when they are switched off, so ensure you test them when unplugged. Also turn off all other wireless devices like smartphones and tablets when they're not in use.

5. **PPE.** Install a Blushield plug-in device.

Smart appliances

The 'internet of things' has arrived. Almost every new appliance you purchase for your home – air-conditioner, washing machine, dryer, oven, fridge, blender, alarm clock, etc. – will be 'smart' and able to talk to your smartphone and smart meter. The power transmitter on these appliances connects to your smart meter via wi-fi.

The solutions I've listed above for wi-fi devices also apply to smart appliances – though the best option is not to buy them in the first place.

Baby monitors

One of my least favourite inventions is the wireless DECT baby monitor. Sometimes the highest levels of harmful EMFs measured in a home are coming from a baby monitor right next to a sleeping infant. Use a wired baby monitor, or wire your DECT baby monitor using an adapter kit. A new baby monitor by SmartNOVA claims to use 97 per cent less radiation than the normal DECT baby monitors. I have not measured one of these devices yet, but it looks promising.

Before you hand a child a device such as a smartphone, tablet or laptop, please set it to aeroplane mode and switch off Bluetooth. I predict that one day, giving a wireless device to a small child will be considered child abuse.

Microwave ovens

The microwaves that leak out of a microwave oven are very strong, and some of the newer microwaves have energy-saving features that add to the EMFs. Microwaves can also alter the chemical composition of your food. Use an oven instead to heat your food, even though it takes longer.

Power lines

Typical sources of (AC) magnetic fields include electricity towers, appliances (at point sources) and wiring errors. The most glaring issues are sometimes from repairable wiring errors.

The power line test for magnetic EMFs, by the way, demonstrates a very important concept – that distance is your friend. The amount of radiation humans absorb decreases very rapidly with distance: it's called the 'inverse square law'. Double the distance means half the exposure. Going back to our case-study family, Mum notes that this is not the case, though, for readings from wireless sources (RF or microwave EMFs), which appear to drop off more linearly.

Electricity towers

Electricity towers are big sources of AC magnetic fields, which are arguably the most dangerous form of EMFs, and homes should be sited at least 150 metres from the larger 400 kV transmission towers. For power distribution lines in suburban streets, a distance of 15 metres is recommended (www.PowerWatch.org.uk). I recommend measuring the field with a Gauss meter, however, since field strength can vary.

Appliance points

Anything that runs on electricity, including all electrical appliances, is a source of magnetic fields. However, for most household appliances, observing a one-metre distance is usually enough for safety (1 mG), since the strength of these fields decreases quickly with distance from the source. A bedside alarm clock or radio, for example, typically measures about 50 mG directly at the source, 2 mG at 30 cm away and 0.6 mG at 50 cm.

Wiring

Wiring errors, such as connecting the neutrals/return wiring of two different branch circuits (also known as 'paralleled neutrals'), can create large areas of high AC magnetic fields. These decrease linearly with distance, unlike point sources, which decrease much more quickly.

Another common error is making neutral to earthing connections outside of the main service panel. Wiring errors are more common in older homes and should be corrected by a licensed electrician. Again, it's always best to check your house with a Gauss meter before and afterward.

Cars

EMFs have always been present in cars – principally in the form of magnetic fields. However, in the 21st century, much of the technology that has improved our driving experience has also increased our exposure to EMFs in cars. Along with the obvious culprits like wi-fi and Bluetooth installations, this includes RF-ID tags on parts, tyre pressure monitors, wireless car alarm systems, blind spot reversing radar and much more. EHS suffers are best advised to purchase vehicles with minimum electronics, like old diesel four-wheel drives. The rest of us can place a Blushield device in the console.

Light and lifestyle changes

Dad from the family introduced earlier began getting up early in the morning to walk the dog barefoot in the park to ensure he got a healthy dose of morning light and grounding. He also made sure he had some exposed skin during the walk, by rolling up his sleeves and not wearing a hat. He also stopped wearing sunglasses. He's been so impressed with the improvement in how he feels, he now insists that his wife and son join him. The teenage daughter decided she would join in as well to fight her morning blues, as she couldn't cope with how happy the rest of the family was when they arrived home for breakfast.

The whole family now has blue-light-blocking glasses to wear if they turn on the lights in the evening or watch TV. Mum has also become obsessed with mitochondrial health, making seafood the family's main source of protein to ensure they get healthy amounts of DHA, and changing to drinking spring water from the mountains.

Vitamin D levels

There's a wonderful free app called Dminder (dminder.onto metrics.com) that takes into consideration all the variables to calculate how much sun exposure you need to produce enough vitamin D each day. Remember that your body can only produce vitamin D from UVB rays, typically available for most Australians from the mid to late morning through to mid to late afternoon. If you live 35 degrees' latitude from the equator you can get vitamin D every day of the year, but the further you live from the equator, the less vitamin D-producing time there is. Dminder factors in your location and advises when your next opportunity will be to get some sun exposure.

The app also considers the amount of clothing you wear, as less clothing increases the opportunity for production of vitamin D. Skin pigmentation also matters, with dark-skinned people requiring six times more UVB exposure. Overweight and obese people require more exposure, too, as vitamin D is stored in fat layers. Age also reduces absorption: by the age of 50, you need twice the time in the sun to get the same amount of vitamin D.

The app also has a burn counter that calculates the optimal time for vitamin D while ensuring you don't get sunburnt. I can't recommend Dminder highly enough.

School

Mum has lobbied the school without luck over their use of wireless technologies. She continues to try to convince other parents to join the cause by explaining her own family's success in improving their health, and has joined the www.wifi-in-schools-australia.org initiative.

* * *

This case study combines the experiences of a number of different families I've personally been involved with. I'm not a doctor and cannot give medical advice, but I can say that these families are very happy and healthy now, after taking measures to minimise their exposure to manmade EMFs and increase their exposure to full-spectrum sunlight.

TWELVE

The new technological solutions

'Technology like art is a soaring exercise of
the human imagination.'

—*Daniel Bell*

WE can use technology in order to aid us in understanding
the impact our innovations have on human well-being.
The fact is, with technology, we should be able to do this faster,
and design homes, spaces and technologies that promote our
well-being – not just our safety, but also our longevity. And
fortunately, people have taken steps towards this, particularly in
finding control measures to reduce the adverse effects.

In this chapter, I want to introduce some technological
solutions that I believe are some of the best solutions to the
technological problems we face, for the following reasons:

- **They are portable.** You can carry them with you with ease. The last thing you want to have to do is to lug a backpack full of stuff wherever you go – if a solution is intrusive to your life, then it will just create more stress.
- **They are non-invasive.** In other words, you don't need an intravenous needle or anything like that to receive their benefits.
- **They are powerful.** They are effective – if they were weak solutions, there would be no point using them. It would be like trying to warm yourself in subzero temperatures with a lit match.
- **They are proven.** They work at a biological level, with the forces of nature. In an ideal world, I would like to see more hard scientific evidence that they work, but I'm sure that will come with time. And we are not in a position to wait for the government to fund universities to do studies – people are getting sick, and safe solutions like these that have sound experiential case study evidence and plant and animal trials behind them should be implemented now.
- **They are cost-effective.** The benefits of any device have to outweigh the costs, and devices must be priced at a level that the general population can afford. Think about it – if solutions are only available to millionaires, then we would have a huge problem.

These solutions are easy to implement and greatly reduce the amount of work you have to do to protect yourself. Now, alone, are they going to be perfect? No. You'll still have to eliminate harmful EMF sources wherever possible, limit your blue light exposure and incorporate other solutions like the ones discussed in the previous chapter.

Blushield technology

So, what is Blushield technology? It's the most advanced EMF protection I have found to date. I expect the Russians may have developed similar or maybe even superior technology but, if so, it has yet to make into western markets. I don't make this bold claim lightly – I've researched, tested and assessed the efficacy of countless technologies.

If you remember, according to the hierarchy of controls, the best way to control a hazard is to eliminate it completely. But in our connected world, eliminating exposure to EMFs is almost impossible. Blushield, however, is 'personal protective equipment' that operates as close as we can get to minimising the adverse effects of harmful EMFs.

The technology provides protection against common sources of EMFs, both inside homes and offices and externally, including:

- wi-fi routers and enabled devices
- mobile phone towers and mobile phones
- smart and electrical meters
- power lines and poor house wiring
- household appliances (cordless phones, microwave ovens, TVs, baby monitors, etc.).

I've included a couple of images of the Blushield products on the next page.

I won't geek you out on the fine details of how it works, but basically the device follows natural laws to emit a symphony of coherent frequencies within the natural range for human beings. Our bodies respond to the Blushield's natural, coherent frequencies rather than to incoherent and harmful EMFs. Put simply, your body will be made invisible to harmful EMFs.

Figure 12.1: Blushield Tesla Cube

Figure 12.2: Blushield Tesla Portable

Let's take look at the testing results now. Testimonials are great, but the real proof is in lab results. Blushield fields can't be measured by traditional Gauss meters, RF meters and the like, as the fields work at a sub-atomic cellular level, in the relatively new field of quantum biology – so they can only be evaluated biologically. Blushield is small enterprise without the resources to fund double-blind, randomised trials for publication in peer-reviewed medical journals. We need to see more scientific evidence to be completely sure of the devices' efficacy, but initial trials are super-encouraging.

A Blushield case study

A live blood-cell analysis was performed on a male subject in his mid-thirties who was constantly exposed to high levels of EMFs from being in close proximity to electrical equipment all day and spending a lot of time using computers and game consoles. On top of this, he had a very poor diet and did not exercise. The subject was given a Blushield Portable to carry around with him at all times; a Blushield plug-in model was also installed at his home and kept going 24/7. No other changes were made to his diet or lifestyle during the testing period, which ran from 11 January 2012 until 14 March 2012.

The result? His lymphocytes (white blood cells that form part of the immune system) went from 25 to 15, showing a normalisation of the immune system. The changes are explained in detail in the 'before' and 'after' images of his live blood analysis below. Obvious changes are apparent and the walls of the blood cells have normalised within a very short period of time. In the words of the tester: 'Extremely reduced levels of inflammation and oxidation are amazing considering you have not changed your diet or lifestyle/occupation and had a cold.'

Testing of poultry at poultry farms also showed improved results – but we'll focus on Blushield's benefits to humans. The information is available at www.blueshield-global.com if you're interested.

Figure 12.3: Blushield live blood analysis test results

Blood tests – before Blushield

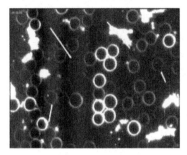

Blood tests – after Blushield

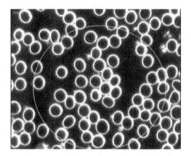

The red cells' membranes are ghosting (exploding) due to their weakened state. Red cells are literally disappearing while being watched during live blood analysis.

Within 2 months the red cells have notably stronger membranes and fewer parasites. Despite the subject having a cold there is a marked improvement in blood quality.

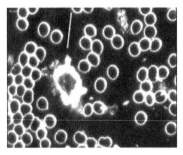

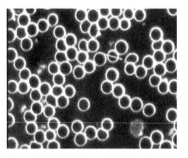

There is a lot of parasite and crystallisation taking place in the blood. Red cells are also bunched together and are of irregular shape.

Crystallisation has ceased and the red cells are of a more regular shape and distribution. A remarkable improvement despite no change in diet or lifestyle.

The Blushield devices tick all the requirements I discussed before:

• **Portable.** You can place the Blushield plug-in cube permanently in your home or office space, and carry the portable device in your pocket – it's about the size of a mobile phone. The cube provides protection up to 90 metres radially, and the portable version provides coverage of up to 3 metres radially – offering more than enough protection. The cube may also benefit your neighbours!

- **Non-invasive.** You plug the cube into an electrical socket, and the portable version is powered by battery. You don't need to plug it into your veins or body in any way – thank goodness.

- **Powerful.** The new Tesla Gold Series uses micro photonic crystals and high-powered multiple waveform technology. Blushield Active EMF Protection uses powerful fields, not weak fields like those from the stickers, pendants or pyramids you may see for sale.

- **Proven.** We just discussed this. One reason why manmade EMFs pose a health risk is that they use a single narrow pulsating frequency (e.g. a mobile phone base station signal), because this is more practical and considerably cheaper. Continual exposure to a single frequency is deleterious to human health in much the same way as eating just one type of food will result in poor nutrition. Blushield uses millions of natural frequencies configured in a symphony of unique, never repeating combinations within the human responsive range to mitigate artificial EMF at a cell level. Frequencies are arranged using nature's rhythms and cycles; namely, the Phi/golden ratio and Fibonacci sequences. Blushield also utilises a pulse/pause cycle, with the device on for about three seconds and off for approximately 30 seconds. As such, the body does not build resistance or aversion to this natural cycle of supportive and nurturing frequencies.

- **Cost-effective.** With its benefits including coherent thinking and overall greater health, the investment in Blushield is easy to justify. Blushield also comes with a 'no questions asked' 60-day money-back guarantee and lifetime warranty.

Basically, if you can't be bothered implementing most of the EMF controls discussed in the previous chapter, and want a simple solution, then Blushield is a great initial step. Of course, I wouldn't advise you to live near communication towers or sleep with your mobile phone under your pillow – you have to use your common sense. But if you want one quick and easy solution to implement, this is it.

In Chapter 11, I mentioned this technology as a PPE control measure. Here's the story of how one of the actual mothers whom the case study is based on discovered Blushield. One day, Mum walks into her yoga studio and, before she even lays her mat down, unexpectedly finds she feels very coherent. Her energy levels rise and become stable, she is thinking more clearly, and she remembers what it feels like to be alive and vibrant. She thinks maybe she's just having a good day and has overdosed on morning sun, so her dopamine levels are through the roof. But she wonders if it's somehow the studio space that has changed, and when she talks to the yoga teacher, she asks, 'What is it about this space? It feels different – calmer, more vibrant'. The teacher tells her that she had bought and plugged in a Blushield device a couple of days before, after hearing about it at a yoga conference.

I personally keep a portable Blushield device with me all the time, and it's approved for air travel too. I also have a big cube in my office and in my home. That way, whether I'm in transit or not, I'm always protected from harmful EMFs. What encourages me most about Blushield is the inventor and owner is open to anyone interested in conducting independent research on the products.

The future is bright. The inventor claims that the technology offers opportunities for integration with existing and new digital technology, which means that all technology has the chance to be biologically supportive to human well-being. As you can tell, I'm quite excited about this possibility.

If you have more questions you want answered, visit www.blushield-global.com. The website includes information on how the device works, the scientific evidence, what model may be best for you, how to set it up in your home, and of course how to purchase it.

The Quantlet™

The Quantlet is a patent-pending wearable device in the form of a flexible bracelet that applies light and cold through the skin of the wrist and ultimately to the blood. This product has not yet been publicly released, but you can pre-order it through a crowd-funding campaign.[87]

Using a proprietary set of UV and infra-red wavelengths and other parameters that mimic sunlight, developed by Quantum Dynamics, the Quantlet emits light through the skin and tissue down to the radial and ulnar arteries, as well as the wrist veins. The light triggers targeted, localised and controllable production of nitric oxide, a well-known agent for enhancing physical performance by increasing blood flow.

The Quantlet works to boost energy, overcome fatigue, improve sleep and reduce inflammation, and it provides a wide variety of benefits to personal health and mental and physical performance, including:

- increasing exercise efficiency and capacity, literally at the touch of a button
- extending exercise times, including the time it takes you to reach 50 per cent strength reduction
- achieving a higher peak force in resistance training
- lowering creatine kinase levels (a measure of muscle damage)
- naturally and safely stimulating the production of body and brain chemicals that dramatically increase energy
- attaining a sense of well-being you may have not thought possible.

Without going into great technical detail, the Quantlet works by using a technique called 'photobiomodulation' to deliver multiple frequencies of light into the body. It's a big word, so let's break it down into components:

- 'photo' = light
- 'bio' = life
- 'modulation' = change.

Remember how I talked earlier about 'digesting' light through your eyes? This is another way to digest light, but through the arteries in your wrist. Now, the effects of photobiomodulation were discovered over 40 years ago and have been studied at such prestigious institutions as Harvard and NASA. Photobiomodulation effects depend on the application of the appropriate wavelength and density of light to the target tissues for a specific period of time.

Photobiomodulation has a photochemical effect, much like photosynthesis in plants. (I told you trees and humans had lots in common!) One of the main mechanisms of action occurs inside the mitochondria, the energy power plant inside every cell of a human being.

As you can see, the Quantlet's inventors have really understood health from a biophysics perspective and used technology to help us thrive. See, when industry sees technological advancement and true human well-being as inseparable, you end up with devices such as the Quantlet and Blushield. So exciting!

But I'm not done yet showing off the Quantlet. The device also has a cooling module that uses components called thermoelectric coolers (TECs) that leverage what's called the 'Peltier effect'. Using a solid-state electronic mechanism for cooling removes the need for cooling fluids and minimises the device's footprint.

Physical performance is deeply tied to your body's temperature. When you get hot, your performance suffers, because key respiratory proteins and cellular enzymes change shape and may even malfunction if they overheat, and this impacts certain metabolic processes. Keeping the body cool during exercise or exertion can help you perform better.

But that's not all! Cold thermogenesis, as it is known scientifically, is an exciting new area of research which has recently been shown to have positive effects on thyroid function, fat loss, exercise efficiency and inflammation reduction. Recent studies have found that adults have more brown adipose (fat) tissue than was previously believed, which can significantly increase energy expenditure in response to cold exposure.

If you do a quick internet search, you'll see that there are many health devices on the market that promise amazing results and breakthrough 'cures' for all sorts of issues. The thing is, 99 per cent of these devices have absolutely no research or proven results to back them up. The Quantlet, by contrast, ticks almost all the boxes I discussed before:

- **Portable.** The device just sits on your wrist. Left or right? You choose!

- **Non-invasive.** The device sits on your wrist, it doesn't penetrate your skin. It's easy to use and completely painless – no different to, say, wearing an exercise monitor like a Fitbit – but it's promoting good health rather than damaging it.

- **Powerful.** The Quantlet uses red and infra-red LEDs to obtain a photobiomodulating effect that's just as powerful as that obtained by the invasive intravenous method used by researchers.

- **Proven.** In multiple studies conducted in countries such as Germany, Russia, China and Brazil, investigators have noted that irradiating blood with specific frequencies and intensities of light resulted in improvements in subjects' lipid levels, cholesterol, blood sugar, clotting and immunity.[88] The Quantlet leverages proven medical research and well-established science from some of the most respected institutions in the world. Strikingly, in sports medicine in particular, athletes treated with red and infra-red light have seen increased exercise capacity and longer exercise times, as well as improved biomarkers after exercise (including reduced lactate, creatine kinase and CRP). You can watch a video demonstrating the Quantlet's cooling effects at thequantlet.com.

The only things yet to be confirmed are the Quantlet's patent and release price. Contributors to the crowdfunding campaign paid close to US$750 for a device, so I imagine the retail price will be comparable to the Blushield cube, the most powerful Blushield product available in the market that retails for AUD$990.

You may be thinking at this point that buying devices is too much effort or too costly – but the pay-offs in terms of being able to think clearly, be proactive and have the energy to take on life are huge. Just try them and observe.

THIRTEEN

What I do

'The power to change your life lies in the simplest of steps.'

—*Steve Maraboli*

BEFORE we wrap up this part of the book, let me walk you through a day in my life, to show you how the solutions might work in your life. I use a mix of controls and the technological solutions I shared in Chapter 12. You'll probably want to piece together a hybrid solution as well. The average person living in a shared household and working in an artificial environment such as an office will likely need protection at home, in transit and at work. There are, of course, a great number of alternative solutions you may wish to explore, as well.[89]

Here's what I do:

1. **I got into the habit of waking up and getting morning sun.** Even with amazing new technologies like the Quantlet out there, nothing beats the rays coming from the sun. I expose my face and whole body if I can – about 30 minutes a day

first thing around sunrise is perfect. I go to the beach so that I get both the photons from the sun and the electrons from the sand and minerals from the ocean. If you do any form of exercise, try to do it outdoors in the morning as well, or perhaps take a barefoot walk to your favourite coffee shop.

2. **I replaced all cordless phones in my home with wired versions** – you could, alternatively, buy a low-radiation DECT cordless phone to reduce the amount of waves travelling about.

3. **I open up all the blinds and curtains and some windows and doors** to allow as much sunlight in as possible during daytime. **I don't wear sunglasses during the day either. I also never turn on lights at night** and prefer to use candles. This reduces the effects of blue light and melatonin suppression.

4. **If I have to work with electronic devices at night, I wear amber filter glasses.** (Some say you should also wear them during the day if you're working indoors under artificial lights.) The glasses help reduce the intensity of the blue light getting into your eyes, and reduce the degree to which melatonin is suppressed in your system. I also have f.lux installed on all my computers; and you could enable Night Shift mode on your iPhone if you have one.

5. **At my office, I have full-spectrum lighting and have put blue-blocking acrylic filters on my computer screens.** I take lunch at the park with my shoes off whenever I can, too. Our city office does have wi-fi and my iPhone can detect over a dozen wi-fi networks from companies on other floors and buildings. I have placed two Blushield

cubes to cover the entire 500m^2 office space to help alleviate this situation (see 11 below).

6. **For making calls on my smartphone, I use an 'air tube' headset** or sometimes the speaker, holding the phone at least 30 cm away from my body.

7. **I only turn on my wi-fi router when necessary, typically when visitors require access.** If you aren't using your wi-fi, why have it on? Thankfully, I live in an area where my iPhone cannot receive signals from any neighbours' wi-fi networks.

8. **I use ethernet cables instead of wi-fi.** At home, I use an ethernet cable to connect to the internet, rather than a wireless router. Not everyone loves this option, as you can't just stand up and walk around with your computer. But the extra benefit is that data transmission is much faster.

9. **Our smart meter is located 15 to 20 metres away from any living areas and has been shielded.** This is a big one. Ask your utility company to replace the smart meter if it's already been installed, or opt out of having it installed if you can.

10. **I switch off everything in the bedroom** or don't have any devices in there to begin with. That means phones are in aeroplane mode and in another room, no alarm clock and all lights are off. Sleeping in total darkness promotes melatonin secretion in your body, and helps you rest and recover deeply.

11. **I use both portable and plug-in Blushield devices.** In total, a starter pack costs around $1,000. The portable device I just carry in my pocket or bag whenever I leave the house. I also have a portable in my car. I put the plug-in in the living area of my house, where my family spend most of their

time. At work, I have large Blushield plug-ins to cover our entire office.

12. **I have a 'no tech' day.** I do my best to have at least one day a week when I don't use any technology – no phone, car, computer, and so on.

13. **Last of all, whenever I can, I take a break and get out in nature** – get some sun, get some surf, and put my bare feet on the ground, whether that's on weekends, on holidays or before work. I now know that if it wasn't for my love of the ocean (swimming and diving and connecting with nature), which balanced out my love of technology and working in artificial environments, I probably wouldn't be alive today.

I really wish I had known about these control measures and solutions while my mother was still alive. We could have implemented protocols to improve the heteroplasmy of her mitochondria, had her bathe in morning sun and drink the early morning rays through her eyes. We could have blocked excessive blue light by providing her with amber glasses to wear while watching TV, and implemented other dietary and lifestyle measures. However, it's not too late for the rest of us to benefit. It's not too late for you!

---

86 Angela Stringfellow, 2016, *Cell phone safety: 50 tips on smartphone safety, cell phone safety for kids, and more*, Verizon, <http://tccrocks.com/blog/cell-phone-safety-tips/#ReduceRadiation>

87 Indiegogo, The Quantlet: Human Performance Reimagined, <https://www.indiegogo.com/projects/the-quantlet-your-workout-wellness-optimized#>

88 Tiina Karu, PHD, 2013, *Is It Time to Consider Photobiomodulation as a Drug Equivalent?* <http://www.ncbi.nlm.nih.gov/pmc/articles/PMC3643261/> And Hoon Chung, Tianhong Dai, Sulbha K. Sharma, Ying-Ying Huang, James D. Carroll, and Michael R. Hamblin, 2012, The Nuts and Bolts of Low-level Laser (Light) Therapy, <http://www.ncbi.nlm.nih.gov/pmc/articles/PMC3288797/>

89 Electric Sense website, www.electricsense.com

PART FOUR

SHADOWS IN THE FUTURE

'Man cannot discover new oceans unless he has the courage to lose sight of the shore.'

—*André Gide*

FOURTEEN

Chasing the sun

'Technology…is a queer thing. It brings you great gifts
with one hand, and it stabs you in the back with the other.'

—*C.P. Snow*

D ID you ever try to outrun your shadow? As I child, I did. It's
impossible, though I tried until things got cold, the day got
dark and it was time to go home. The shadow we're facing now,
though, follows you into your house, and it's just getting denser
and denser.

Now, gladly, you know about some workable solutions to this
'shadow' of manmade EMFs and artificial light – especially the
technological solutions such as Blushield and the Quantlet. Why
'especially'? Because although, as we discussed earlier, the most
effective way of dealing with harmful EMFs is eliminating the
source, at the rate wireless technology is advancing and being
rolled out, avoidance measures are not going to be possible for
long. Instead, technologies like Blushield and the Quantlet will
need to continue to evolve to keep up.

Exponential technological change

The rate of technological change is astounding. You may know Moore's law, which states that a doubling of computer processing speed occurs every 18 months. (Gordon E. Moore, the co-founder of Intel and Fairchild Semiconductor, made this observation in 1965.) Ray Kurzweil, the head of engineering at Google, gives us this perspective:

> When I was an undergraduate, we all shared a computer at MIT that took up half of a building ... The computer in your cell phone today is a million times cheaper and a thousand times more powerful.

This continual, exponential increase in computer processing speed generally results in an increase in processing power and a decrease in cost, and with it, vast technological versatility. Think about it: there was a time when 128 MB USB drives cost hundreds of dollars. Now, they cost peanuts, and a one-terabyte hard drive (over a million megabytes) costs around $70.

And look at your phone. Mobile phones were once the size of a brick and could only make phone calls. Now, your phone is a few millimetres thick, fits in your pocket (although, I recommend you don't keep it there!) and functions as a computer, a stereo, a mini TV and video camera, as well as having access to unlimited apps – even one that helps you calculate your vitamin D level. Today, too, a Zimbabwean teenager can have the same smartphone as a Wall Street billionaire – that's the power of exponential technology. Prices get cheaper, technology improves dramatically and everyone gains access.

We're on an exponential trend, and it means that the EMF soup that is submerging humanity and the artificial lighting saturating our systems are only going to get more intense, dense and inescapable. You can't do much today without relying on connected technologies – getting money from the bank, paying for petrol at the petrol station, and buying anything at pretty much any retail outlet requires permission from a machine. Maybe that's why I love shopping at my local organic farmer's market! But let me paint a picture now of the future at home, in the office, at school and even in nature.

Goodbye landlines

An article published on Techwire.net in April 2016[90] reported that US telecommunications giant AT&T is requesting government permission to decommission its landlines in California. With 85 per cent of Californian households no longer having a conventional landline phone, why should AT&T continue spending money to maintain the costly landline infrastructure?

California may be the first to take this route, but you can be sure it won't be the last. Humanity is going wireless. Personally, I feel relieved that I have my Blushield devices!

Increasing interconnection of devices

The modern household can now have all its devices interconnected and communicating, with a number of benefits:

- **An unprecedented level of comfort and automation.**
  Climate control systems can monitor the environment and your living patterns to determine the best settings for you and your family. Imagine walking into your home and having the temperature absolutely perfect without having to do a thing – it's great!

- **Efficiency and savings.** Communication between appliances like your refrigerator, coffee machine, washing machine, lighting, air-conditioning system and water systems allows for optimum functioning while saving a lot of energy. It's more environmentally sustainable and less taxing on your bank account.
- **Tighter security.** You can always check into your home on your mobile devices to make sure everything is okay – and even say hi to your dog. You can also get all security updates automatically. That's peace of mind.

But this degree of connectivity, as you know, comes at a cost – it requires us to constantly swim in thicker and more intense fields of harmful EMFs.

Figure 14.1: A fully integrated and connected household

Virtual and augmented reality

Virtual reality (VR) and augmented reality (AR) involve the use of wireless headsets to enter an imaginary world; you can be entertained as though you were at a live show and educated as though you were at school or a business event. For *Star Trek* fans – the holodeck is here.

By 2017, it's estimated that virtual and augmented reality images will have higher definition than the human eye can see. Essentially, we may be unable to distinguish between reality and illusion. But the point I want to make is, if the quality of the video is so high, a huge amount of data is going to be transferred very fast – and that means intense amounts of EMFs bouncing around in our atmosphere.

People are looking at rolling out VR/AR across all sectors: not just entertainment, but also education, workforce skills development, communications and so on. If that happens, children are going to grow up being educated by devices that fry their brains and bodies and subject them to an excessive amount of blue light. And if you thought it was hard now to get kids off their screens, well, you've seen nothing yet. VR/AR offers gaming on steroids, making it a huge challenge to get kids – and adults – to leave the virtual world and reconnect with nature. It's doesn't bode well.

Future workplaces

So how about the workplace? Well, your wildest imaginings are probably possible, if they're not already being rolled out. First, virtual collaboration may mean you won't ever have to leave your home, depending on the field you work in and your preferences.

In the workplace, everything will be connected – and with so many workers using communication technologies simultaneously in one location, you could probably stick your tongue out and taste the effects of EMFs.

Many workers may also be microchipped, rather than using swipe cards to get in and out of the workplace, drawing even more EMFs towards their bodies. Sound crazy? Once upon a time, this idea would have come out of a science-fiction novel, but the future truly is now. Dr Katherine Albrecht reveals in her book *SPYCHIPS*[91] how RFID technology, if left unchecked, could soon become one of the most powerful surveillance tools in history. In Sweden, workers in a shared office space called Epicenter can have tiny radiofrequency identification (RFID) chips the size of grains of rice embedded in their hands to give them access to the building, photocopiers and lifts – and even to communicate with smartphone apps. Talk about becoming an EMF magnet!

'Smart'... everything!

Human ingenuity has been quick to capitalise on the new 'smart' revolution. The new Oral B Genius 9000 toothbrush connects to your smartphone and takes you on a '28-day plaque journey'. It tells you how long you brush each tooth, while informing you what the weather is like outside. When you leave the house, your smart umbrella and smart wallet will prevent you from losing them by reminding you every time they stray too far from your phone.

Fitbit and Jawbone have already turned half the population into competitive walking windbags. Elvie is a new pelvic-floor exercise tracking contraption which calls itself 'your most personal trainer', and has a matching phone app that tells you how you're doing and allows you to compete online with your friends.

There's ever-increasing competition for the title of 'most ridiculous smart gadget'. Women can buy the Looncup, a silicone menstrual cup with a wireless transmitter that connects to your smartphone to help you track periods. Or maybe you would prefer to use a smart tampon that attaches to a sensor clipped to your underpants: every time the sensor thinks it's time for a new tampon, it alerts your phone. Now, I can't speak from experience, but why would anyone want their body wired up in this way?

For the men, there's NotiFly, an 'invisible user interface' that will tell you when your fly is undone. Seriously. Your pants are woven with electronic fabric, and a flexible circuit board allows a fabric-based switch to be installed in the zipper. To turn the pants on, you zip them up; if the system notices that your zip is down, you get a Bluetooth-based notification to close the gate to the gonad grapes.

To me, smart devices for babies are the most ridiculous and the most harmful of all. There are smart dummies that monitor your baby's temperature, sending the information to your smartphone. There's the Babypod, a wirelessly connected intravaginal device that turns a woman's vagina into a sound system for her unborn child. There are wireless nappies that let you know when the baby needs to be changed, and there's Innotab, a chewable iPad for when your baby is teething.

In many ways, the giddy growth of smart technology is easy to understand. Manufacturers make this stuff because they can, because the technology exists and is quite cheap. And thanks to Indiegogo and other crowdfunding platforms, there's no shortage of tech lovers happy to finance the next crazy idea. Still, the demand for such products remains a puzzle to me: why are people so willing to pay for non-solutions to non-problems?

The more time you spend on wireless gadgets distracting yourself from the joy of living connected to nature, the more you diminish your life force. Hopefully once we get the message out about harmful EMFs and artificial light, people will start making wiser choices for their babies and themselves.

Google in your brain

Perhaps the ultimate sci-fi dream, neural implants, are also poised to become reality. Toyohashi University of Technology researchers have created an implantable, wireless power transmitter that can deliver power to brain–computer implants. KurzweilAI.net reports that the researchers:

> ...plan to integrate additional functions, including amplifiers, analogue-to-digital converters, signal processors, and a radio frequency circuit for transmitting (and receiving) data.

In other words, they want to be able to wirelessly plug Google into your brain.

Megacities and high-rises

Along with artificial lighting and all the devices emitting EMFs and blue light, another worrying trend is the pace at which vertical real estate is increasing. Think about all the high-rise apartments and buildings being erected in cities right now – not only do they block people's access to full-spectrum light from the sun, but they can cast huge shadows across cities, and even across suburbs outside the inner city.

There's a global push for the development of United Smart Cities, driven by the United Nations.[92] I'm seeing my hometown of Sydney gradually increase its high-density housing and promote itself as being a smart city of the future.[93]

The global wi-fi rollout

You might be thinking, 'Surely, though, natural places – the forests and outback – will always offer us and our children plenty of natural light and no or low levels of EMFs, right? We can opt out if we want to, any time we like! We've talked about doing this in previous chapters. Well, the sunlight part may be right, but the part about EMFs is totally wrong.

If you think that in five or ten years you'll be able to avoid EMFs by living in the bush, think again. People in the jungles of the Amazon and in the most remote communities on earth will soon be drenched in EMFs. Let's explore this.

(Almost) country-wide wi-fi in Estonia and Taiwan

Did you know that Estonia, in northern Europe, is nicknamed 'E-stonia' because of its wi-fi penetration rates? According to Statistics Estonia, in the first quarter of 2010, 75 per cent of the 1.34 million people in the country used the internet.[94] Estonia has declared internet access a basic human right, and has digitally streamlined an unprecedented number of public services for its citizens and businesses. Each citizen has an ID that can be used to access their health records and prescriptions, pay for public transport, view their children's school grades and even vote. The country also has a thriving IT start-up culture.

Wireless internet is almost everywhere in Estonia, and it is almost always free and fast. Wi-fi access points can be found in most public locations – parks, squares, pubs, cafés, restaurants, airports, trains, bus stations. And it's often possible to access the internet in what seems like a remote location, on a beach or in a forest.

Similarly, Taiwan has more than 4,000 free, government-backed wi-fi access points dotted around its small island, even in places you wouldn't think you would find a signal.

Figure 14.2: Wi-fi in remote areas

Balloons, drones, satellites and the 'Rising Billions'

Did you know that tens of billions of dollars are being deployed with the aim of rolling out wireless internet connections to the whole world? These are some of the scariest initiatives from the perspective of harmful EMFs. The four major players are Google, Facebook, SpaceX and OneWeb, a company with investors that include Richard Branson's Virgin Group, Qualcomm and Coca-Cola.

Google and Project Loon

The slogan on Google's Project Loon website (solveforx.com/loon) is 'Balloon-powered internet for everyone', and its mission is to set up a high-altitude balloon network to provide wi-fi internet access to those living in rural and remote areas – over half of the world's population. Project Loon's balloons float in the stratosphere, twice as high up as aeroplanes and above the effects of weather.

Around 30 balloons were launched in 2013 in New Zealand as part of a pilot experiment. In March 2016, the US Federal Communications Commission granted Google permission to float their balloons in 50 American states.

Facebook and Internet.org

Facebook plans to bring web access to underserved countries through its Internet.org initiative, and is investigating using drones, lasers and satellites to provide internet connection. Facebook CEO and founder Mark Zuckerberg announced:

> Our goal with Internet.org is to make affordable access to basic internet services available to every person in the world.[95]

The initiative's Aquila drone prototype has the wingspan of a Boeing 737 but weighs less than 500 kilograms; powered by solar panels on its wings, it will be able to fly at altitudes of more than 60,000 feet for months at a time.

SpaceX

Elon Musk's SpaceX company is working on a project that would use around 700 small satellites to provide internet to the planet, focusing, again, on rural and developing areas. According to

Musk, the project can be expected to deploy in 'sooner than five years', with a price-tag of $10 billion.[96]

OneWeb

Not to be left out, Richard Branson's Virgin Group, telecommunications company Qualcomm, Coca-Cola and a number of other global heavy-hitters have invested in OneWeb.[97] The company plans to launch 648 mini-satellites to operate at an altitude of 1,200 km, each capable of delivering at least 8 gigabits per second of throughput, to provide worldwide internet access to homes and mobile platforms.[98] Satellite launches are on schedule to begin in 2017.[99]

The 'Rising Billions'

As Xprize CEO Peter Diamandis wrote in *The Huffington Post* in June 2015, the most dramatic change in our global economy is set to occur between 2016 and 2025, when three to five billion new consumers will come online, mostly from developing nations – bringing tens of trillions of new dollars. He has called these new consumers, the 'Rising Billions'. In 2016, at the time of writing, only 3.5 billion people worldwide are connected to the internet.[100] By around 2020, Diamandis writes, he expects that the entire world will be connected. And he points out:

> The Rising Billions are not coming online like we did 20 years ago with a 9600 modem on AOL. They're coming online with a 1 Mbps connection and access to the world's information on Google, cloud 3D printing, Amazon Web Services, artificial intelligence with Watson, crowdfunding, crowdsourcing and more.[101]

Figure 14.3: Internet users worldwide

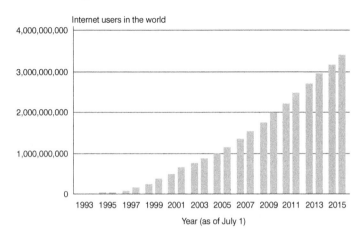

Source: http://www.internetlivestats.com/internet-users/

The possibility of humanity's seven billion-plus minds being able to collaborate using globally available internet is staggering. Think about the impact the Rising Billions will have on innovation! And with global internet, things like disaster aid can be provided much more effectively. That's the bright sun of hope that humanity is chasing with the global wi-fi rollout. However, its shadow is harmful EMFs.

FIFTEEN

Bees don't lie

'If the bee disappeared off the surface of the globe then
man would only have four years of life left. No more bees, no more
pollination, no more plants, nor more animals, no more man.'

—*Canadian Bee Journal in 1941*

EINSTEIN famously said that if the bees disappear, we disappear. In this chapter, I want to briefly widen your view beyond humanity. Because EMFs don't only do damage to humans – they damage all living things. In particular, EMFs damage bees. And unfortunately, damage to bees has big repercussions for us – no living thing is an island, we are all interconnected.

Bees are some of the hardest working creatures on the planet, responsible for pollinating about one-sixth of all flowering plant species worldwide, and approximately 400 different agricultural types of plants. Pollination is the process in which pollen from the male part of a flower is applied to the female part of a flower, allowing the plant to create a seed, nut or fruit – to grow new plants. Now, many plants can use the wind to pollinate, but more often than not, animal intervention is needed. Without bees, our everyday food supply would diminish: it's estimated that at least one-third of our staple foods would no longer be available.

Here's the scary thing with regards to bees and EMFs. An experiment done in Sweden[102] exposed some bee hives to mobile phone radiation for 10 minutes a day for 10 days, and others to none. The control hives, the unaffected ones, were fine. The bees from the hives exposed to the radiation eventually didn't come back – leaving their queen, eggs and immature worker bees without food. The colonies eventually collapsed and the hives died.

This experiment was repeated 83 times and the results were similar. Dr George Carlo, who headed the Cellular Telecommunications Industry Association's $25 million mobile phone research project, made this comment about bees:

> The colony collapse disorder has occurred concurrently on four continents within a very short time frame. If the reason was biological or chemical, there would be a pattern of epidemic spread – we would be able to trace the spread of bee disappearance or Colony Collapse Disorder from a source similar to the spread of SARS a few years ago. That is not the case. The condition has hit each continent at roughly the same time. That would mean the cause has to have hit the continents at the same time as well. Mobile phones meet that criterion.

So what's going to happen to our friendly bees when EMFs penetrate all natural environments all over the world? I think you can join the dots. Bees are a single point of failure for humanity. If they go, we go too.

What can we do? After reading Part 3 of this book, you know what you can do personally to avoid the harmful effects of living in a technologically connected world. But what about the rest of the planet? I recommend, firstly, that you subscribe to the emfwarriors.com website to stay posted on trends. Next, share this book and share the message.

Additionally, if you or people in your networks have an entrepreneurial bent – well, it's up to us entrepreneurs to have ongoing dialogue and stimulate innovation that can solve the big problems the planet is facing. In the next chapter, I share the type of thinking needed for us to thrive in the future.

SIXTEEN

For the entrepreneurs – flow rather than force

'The only way to make sense out of change is to plunge
into it, move with it, and join the dance.'

—*Alan W. Watts*

AT 10 years of age, I was in a boxing demonstration as part of
my primary school speech night. Unfortunately for me, I
was outclassed – but I knew I could take a few blows and thought
I could finish on top of my opponent as he gradually got tired
from hitting me so much. I was wrong. The referee pulled the
plug on the match out of concern for the number of blows to the
head I was copping. In the same way, if we try to just weather the
effects of EMFs and artificial lighting, or even go head to head
with them in the ring, as in opposing industry and trying to get
government legislation to change, we won't win. Nope. It's a
recipe for disaster.

In today's world, industry leads and directs government policy. Politicians are compromised by generous campaign funding (on and off the books) and by skilful and discreet lobbying. University professors don't dare risk their tenure by biting the hands that feed them their research grants, either. There is only one force that the establishment is terrified of – and that is basically angry mothers. They have always led the most successful campaigns: like the campaigns against genetically modified organisms, violent video games, drink-driving and violence. So, if you want to buck the system and bring about lasting change, you must find a win/win strategy and have community support and involvement.

Aikido thinking

What I'd like to suggest is an alternative way of thinking as entrepreneurs and human beings. I like to use the 'aikido' analogy, instead of boxing. Aikido is a Japanese martial art; the practitioner's objective is to defend themselves while disarming and also protecting their attacker from injury. The philosophy is to unify the practitioner with life energy or the harmonious spirit; turning, flowing movements are used to redirect the momentum of an opponent's attack.

Applying this principle in the field of technology would mean that, rather than abolish technology, we preserve its function and service to us but simultaneously also defend ourselves from the blows it can deal. That means we get the benefits, but we don't suffer the repercussions. You have seen the perfect example of this in Blushield technology. Instead of finding yourself a cabin in the bush or a happy Faraday cage to live in, you can use the Blushield, which generates its own coherent and natural frequencies for our bodies to respond to instead of to harmful EMFs. You can live in a harmful EMF-rich environment and still maintain your well-being. Genius! The Quantlet is similar, effectively identifying deficiencies of full-spectrum light in your body and helping fill the gap.

These are both perfect examples of aikido thinking. It's about looking at health through a physicist's lens, applying the findings like an engineer, and presenting solutions to the masses through entrepreneurship.

The need for continuing development of solutions

Existing solutions like Blushield and the Quantlet will continue to work, however, *only* if they continue to evolve at the same exponential rates as technology and keep pace with it. I believe they will, and will extend even further. The inventor of Blushield, for example, believes he can 'aikido' the harmful EMFs emitted by telecommunication towers by retrofitting the towers with Blushield technology. Receivers would then also have to be inserted into smart devices to receive the coherent fields. Now, this is a massive undertaking, but if I was board member of a tele-communication company, I would certainly be looking at this and other technologies that could help mitigate potential risks to my company.

Our work is not done yet. It's never done – it's going to be an ongoing journey as our civilisation advances into the future. We need to educate and inspire entrepreneurs, researchers, scientists and inventors to start looking for solutions to the problems of manmade EMFs and artificial light.

We are not going to give up our technology and the amazing advancements we have achieved. Instead we must focus on inventing safe technology. We want to exemplify what it is to innovate with respect and consideration for the health of humanity and Mother Earth – which are inseparable.

Problems that are calling for solutions

I believe, just as Richard Branson does, that entrepreneurs can drive huge and positive changes on the planet. My belief is that without a transaction there can be no change. For thousands of years,[103] business has been the primary vehicle for delivering solutions and making a difference to people's lives. If you put on the hat of an entrepreneur, and combine that with a biophysics understanding of technology and human well-being, there are huge opportunities available. Here are a few problems that I can see calling for solutions.

'Organic' tech safe electronic store

Just like our appetite for organic food is at record levels I predict the demand for tech safe electronics will be in high demand. Mothers will demand baby monitors that do not harm their babies and low RF-EMF emitting communication and entertainment devices for themselves and their kids. The store will stock shielding materials and have well EMF trained electricians who can test and ameliorate dirty electricity in homes and hard wire all your devices.

Better screens

The immediate problem that I see needs solving is how to filter out excessive blue light from screens so they better represent full-spectrum sunlight. We're learning, through quantum biology, the importance of the eye not just as a camera but also as a receiver of information that filters through to our brain and of electrical signals that are sent through the body to control our bodily processes. The market for better screens for our computers and phones is potentially worth billions.

VR/AR headsets

As we saw in Chapter 14, we're about to see an explosion of headsets for virtual and augmented reality (VR/AR) applications. These will be used by gamers, students at school, conference delegates and in many applications in business. Literally billions of people are about to be wearing headsets that are harmful to their health – talk about a massive business opportunity for talented light designers and engineers!

Communication towers and mobile devices

If frequencies found in nature can be generated as coherent fields by Blushield or similar technology, imagine what would happen if all mobile telecommunication towers and devices used such frequencies. Wow! I wouldn't have to try to stop my step-daughter from using her smartphone every day – she could text using her double-thumb technique to her heart's content. Currently, Blushield is like a lotus in a swamp. But what if we could turn the swamp of signals into a beautiful river of coherent fields?

Without such technologies, my guess is that very few people will be able to live long term in our newly created 'smart' cities.

Vehicles

Similar coherent-field technology will be required for electronic vehicles, especially when autonomous vehicles hit the market.

Planes, trains, buses and ferries will all need such technology as larger and larger proportions of the population suffer from a host of modern diseases.

Testing for heteroplasmy

Dr Doug Wallace's bombshell discovery that the condition of mitochondrial DNA, measured as percentage of mutant mitochondrial DNA (heteroplasmy), is a primary reason for the majority of modern diseases is just beginning to spread among the health profession. I had always wondered why, after so many billions of dollars have been spent on the human genome project and years of DNA research, we haven't seen many major breakthroughs. Now we know the reason!

The problem for health professionals and patients, however, is that there is no simple diagnostic test for mitochondrial health. Whoever invents a test for measuring percentage of heteroplasmy is in for a huge windfall.

* * *

Think about the marketing point of difference if you provide technologies that do more good to people's health than harm, preserving and supporting their longevity. With an ageing population who want to maintain an active lifestyle into their later years, this approach is a gold mine for entrepreneurs.

Arthur Schopenhauer told us that all truth is first denied and then violently challenged, before it's accepted as self-evident. We're currently at stage two, being violently opposed. The great news is, between stage two and stage three lies billions of dollars of opportunity – and the opportunity to positively impact billions of lives.

Part summary

- **Technological advancement is moving at light speed.** So we need light-speed solutions. The technological solutions I've discussed in this book, Blushield and the Quantlet, are a great start. However, we must be aware of upcoming trends which cannot be reversed, and stay abreast of technologies that are keeping up with the problems.

- **High-density multi-storey housing in megacities is making access to full-spectrum light more and more difficult.** This is a scary one, because really, no matter how good the technology, nothing beats full-spectrum sunlight for recharging our cellular batteries and regulating our natural biological processes.

- **Share the information and stimulate dialogue.** Awareness is the first step. The more conversation around the problem and consideration it's given, the more it will embed itself into the psyche of our society. Again, I believe that environmental sciences and industry must collaborate to ensure the longevity of our race and of our precious Mother Earth.

- **Everything on earth is connected.** For one to thrive, we all have to thrive. The bees demonstrate this best. We're part of a living, breathing system, and can no longer afford to look at technology and our innovations as something separate to this. For anything we create to last, I believe it must add to the system, rather than take from it.

90   Samantha Young, 2016, *AT&T Wants to Decommission Landlines in California*, Techwire.net, <http://www.techwire.net/legislation/att-wants-to-decommission-landlines-in-california.html>
91   Lee, Chelsea, 2011, *Books and Book Chapters: What to Cite*, American Psychological Association website, <http://blog.apastyle.org/apastyle/2011/02/books-and-book-chapters-what-to-cite.html>
92   UNECE, United Smart Cities, <http://www.unece.org/housing/smartcities.html>
93   Future Cities Collaborative, Inspiring Future City Leaders, <http://www.futurecities.org.au/>
94   Internet in Estonia, Wikipedia, https://en.wikipedia.org/wiki/Internet_in_Estonia
95   Mark Zuckerberg Facebook post, <https://www.facebook.com/zuck/posts/10101991410913361:2>
96   Ashlee Vance, *Revealed: Elon Musk's Plan to Build a Space*, Bloomberg Technology, <http://www.bloomberg.com/news/articles/2015-01-17/elon-musk-and-spacex-plan-a-space-internet>
97   One Web website, <http://oneweb.world>
98   Peter B. de Selding, 2015, *Competition To Build OneWeb Constellation Draws 2 U.S., 3 European Companies*, <http://spacenews.com/competition-to-build-oneweb-constellation-draws-2-u-s-3-european-companies/>
99   Peter B. de Selding, 2016, *One year after kickoff, OneWeb says its 700-satellite constellation is on schedule*, http://spacenews.com/one-year-after-kickoff-oneweb-says-its-700-satellite-constellation-is-on-schedule/
100 Internet Live States website, <http://www.internetlivestats.com/internet-users/>
101 Peter Diamandis, 2015, *The 'Rising Billion' New Consumers Will Arrive by 2020*, The World Post, http://www.huffingtonpost.com/peter-diamandis/rising-billion-consumers_b_7008160.html
102 Sainudeen Sahib, *Electromagnetic Radiation (EMR) Clashes with Honey Bees International*, 2011, Journal of Environmental Sciences Vol. 1, No. 5.
103 Hubert Howe Bancroft, 1896, *The Book of Wealth: Achievements of Civilization*.

SEVENTEEN

How much proof is enough?

'A demand for scientific proof is always a formula for inaction and delay and usually the first reaction of the guilty ... in fact scientific proof has never been, is not and should not be the basis for political and legal action.'

—*From* Tobacco explained: the truth about the tobacco industry in its own words *(Clive Bates and Andy Rowell, World Health Organization)*

ASBESTOS, a material composed of millions of microscopic fibres, was once used in almost all housing construction. (It was also used thousands of years ago, but we're not going to look that far back!) However, the prolonged inhalation of asbestos fibres causes serious and fatal illnesses including lung cancer, mesothelioma and asbestosis. The accumulated asbestos fibres scar the lungs, and the scar tissue is hard and inflexible, stopping the lungs from functioning properly. When you take away someone's breath, you take away their life.

Why was asbestos used? Well, why is anything used by humans? Because it was useful. It helped with electrical insulation, building insulation, sound absorption and fire resistance, and it was cost-effective. Its use increased through most of the 20th century; it was so commonly used that it's likely that everyone alive today has had some asbestos exposure.

It was a seemingly great invention that had a big dark side. Even today, it's an ongoing concern for manufacturers, insurers and people in the built environment. Remediation is costly, and it will take decades to fully remove asbestos from society. Worse, there are records dating back to Roman times that show evidence of asbestos illness, and if manufacturers had researched its history they may have avoided many deaths and expensive lawsuits.

But when scientists exposed the health hazards of asbestos, guess what? Their claims were violently opposed due to the implications they would have for business and industry.

The asbestos story is a classic example of a 'frog in boiling water' situation – if you heat the water gradually instead of suddenly, the frog won't jump out of the pot, but will boil to death. It can take between five and twenty years before asbestos fibre inhalation starts affecting a person's health, but when they do, victims face an agonising death. There is no cure. You can imagine what an outrage this caused when the courts and legislation caught up with it. It was one of the longest, most expensive mass torts in US history.

Why didn't the corporations do their best to manage the risk and inform the public about it? Sadly, for most companies, financial gain is of higher importance than safety. It sounds scary to say that, and it sounds like I'm a pessimist, but unfortunately, history speaks for itself. In Australia, the key player in asbestos mining and manufacturing was James Hardie Industries Limited. In May 2012, the High Court of Australia found that seven former James Hardie non-executive directors misled the stock exchange over the asbestos victim's compensation fund. The 2009 book *Killer Company* and the 2012 TV docu-drama *Devil's Dust* recount the company's actions.

And other examples of things that 'seemed like a good idea at the time' are easy to find. Think of thalidomide, marketed as a gentle sleeping pill and anti-nausea medication, safe even for pregnant women, which caused thousands of babies worldwide to be born with malformed limbs. Think of tobacco and the way that the tobacco industry has denied smoking's links with cancer for decades.

When the electric car was invented, the petrochemical industry responded aggressively because it was a threat to their business. Similarly, as I mentioned in the introduction to this book, when I proved that lead in paint was killing dogs and poisoning children in Sydney, industry tried to pin it on lead petrol, since property values are a sacred cow in Australia.

Another and more recent example is Uber – violently opposed by the taxi industry for obvious reasons. More often than not, Uber offers its consumers better value for money and more convenience. Their mobile application is great! It has become a billion-dollar company without owning any cars itself, just its technology infrastructure (its platform and website).

Dr Maryanne Demasi, 2016

At the time of writing, industry is violently opposing the idea that EMFs are harmful. In the recent ABC *Catalyst* program 'Wi-Fried?'[104] Dr Maryanne Demasi explored whether wireless devices could be putting people's health at risk. The synopsis couldn't have been worded better:

> Could wi-fi enabled devices be harmful to our health? You cannot see it or hear it but wi-fi blankets our homes, our schools and our cities...

It was a very controversial show, sparking heated debate. Take a look at the response in the media:

- 'Scientists slam Catalyst mobile cancer link' – Nick Sas, *The West Australian*, 17 February 2016
- 'Experts, audience slam ABC *Catalyst*'s report on "Wi-Fi danger"' – Signe Dean, SBS Online, 19 February 2016
- '... it was scientifically bankrupt,' Professor Bernard Stewart told *Crikey*. 'It was biased, and little short of misleading and deceptive' – Myriam Robin, *Crikey*, 17 February 2016
- '*Catalyst* host Maryanne Demasi in the business of advocacy, not journalism' – Jonathan Holmes, *The Age*, 24 February 2016

The mainstream media conveniently used a previous ABC investigation on statin drugs to discredit Dr Maryanne Demasi's report. In other words, they attacked her on a small point, and used this angle to discredit all her work. Rather than debate the issue at hand, namely is wi-fi harmful, the media skewed their arguments directly at Dr Demasi's credibility and previous stories that caught the ire of the ABC. To read more about the scientific response to this program visit www.ehtrust.org.[105]

Andrew Marino's book is called *Going Somewhere*. My take is that those protecting the truth from coming out should write a book and call it *Hiding Something*. It's orchestrated so intelligently and so immediately, it's kind of like that kid in school who, when the teacher says, 'Who stole the money on my table?' responds with an immediate 'Wasn't me! Don't look at me.' Of course, all the other kids know he's at fault. Taking the immediate defensive position often gives people the sign that you are hiding something.

In the coming years, the key to our well-being and longevity is transparency. Government and health and radiation agencies may say there is no evidence of harm from EMFs, but there is a big distinction between that and saying something is safe. The number of scientists who are becoming concerned about the effects of wi-fi and technology is just too big to ignore.

If you too decide that EMFs are a problem, your life might just get a bit controversial as well, I warn you. It can put you at odds with your nearest and dearest, as they are the ones you are going to want to tell! But the most responsible decision to make for the human race is to tell them what you believe the truth to be, and get working on solutions.

The optimist in me wants to believe that companies will take action to do the right thing. However, the realist in me sees that they are motivated by financial gain and by the need to protect their downside – in particular to protect themselves from being sued. I understand this to some extent. I've built businesses and had to make difficult decisions. But it's not just the bottom line at stake, it's people's lives. It is up to leaders to navigate coura-geously and clearly through chaotic situations. A lot of people's fates hang on their decisions.

We can't rely on the powers that be to 'do something' about artificial light and harmful EMFs. We have to take the steering wheel and divert ourselves from the threats we face. Unless we drive change from the bottom up, solutions will only be delayed. The process of demonstrating scientific proof, having it peer reviewed, issuing the findings and implementing solutions is arduous enough as it is.

Out of recognition comes opportunity

I'm not anti-industry nor am I anti-businesses that make a lot of money, or I wouldn't have started a multimillion-dollar company of my own. But when questions are raised, they should be investigated, no matter how dark the findings could be. When we face our problems head on and put our innovative heads together, I believe we can profit and prosper as a whole, without a win/lose scenario. Industry and entrepreneurs should be encouraged to come up with solutions.

If I could go back in time, for example, I would have invested in and backed all asbestos-remediation businesses that were coming up with innovative methods and technologies to safely remove asbestos. They would have made me millions of dollars, created jobs for hundreds of people, and all the while created safer living environments.

The economic environment should be driven by businesses that succeed by having us all succeed! We need a win/win model – providing a return to the investor, a return to the economic system, and a return to the community and the planet. And the faster we bring issues to light, the more chance we give our human family to progress and thrive. So let's explore the negative effects of the technologies of artificial lighting and wireless frequencies *now*. No one should have to wait 30 years to find out whether their health will deteriorate to a near-irreversible level.

As a scientist and an entrepreneur, I feel that innovators should always put the interests of human well-being and a deep respect for the planet first and foremost when developing new technology. If we take that approach, the future can be better than we could ever imagine.

---

104 https://www.youtube.com/watch?v=z5ZOJZQbkmI
105 http://ehtrust.org/wifried-scientific-response-to-criticisms-of-abc-catalyst-program-on-wifi-health-concerns/

Conclusion

As much as this book has been about technology, I want to leave you with this thought:

> Absolutely nothing humanity (or some off-world intelligence!) can create will improve human health and longevity more than reconnecting with our mother planet and father sun.

My wish is the solutions in this book, and the thinking behind them, will serve you and your loved ones so you can preserve your health now and into the future.

And despite the many dark trends knocking on our doors today, I believe the future is brighter than it looks. There are so many great initiatives out there from conscious businesses and enterprises – I believe that technology can work *with* the laws of nature to help us maintain a healthy coexistence on this precious gem we call earth.

Light and the human eye

Let's zoom in on what is really going on when someone 'sees'. If you could watch things in slow motion, and on a nanoscale (a smaller than microscopic scale), you would see beams of light from the morning sun entering the person's eyes. If you then pause the beams and take a closer look as they enter his or her eyes and hit the retinas, you'd see that the human eye contains 127 photoreceptors called rods and 7 million called cones. These tiny structures convert the light into electrical impulses, which are sent to the person's brain at a speed of over 300 kilometres per hour.

These electrical signals travel along the optic nerve and through the brain – through the pituitary gland, hypothalamus and pineal gland to the visual cortex at the back of the brain, producing vision. The person can then see, say, the ocean or trees or whatever they're looking at.

But it doesn't stop at vision, as you can see from Figure A-1 below. From the brain, the electrical signals travel down along the spinal cord, reaching all organs, glands and systems, muscles and bones –communicating with and impacting on all parts of the body and promoting normal, healthy bodily function. They also affect the person's body clock – and when the body clock is in sync with the natural day/night cycle, their body will sing with vitality.

In this way, light entering through a person's eyes regulates or deregulates the majority of their life processes.

Figure A-1 Light passing through the eyes

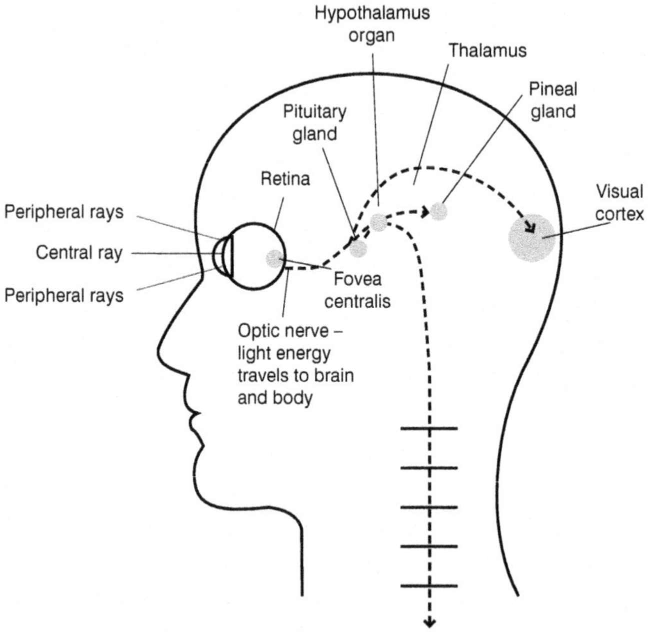

Further reading

Light

John N. Ott. *Health and Light: The extraordinary Study that Shows How light Affects Your Health and emotional well-being.* Ariel Press, 2000 ISBN 10: 0898040981
ISBN 13: 9780898040982

Richard Hobday. *The healing sun: Sunlight and health in the 21st century.* Findhorn Press, 2000 ISBN: 1-899171-97-5

Dr Jacob Liberman. *Light: Medicine of the Future: How We Can Use It to Heal Ourselves NOW.* Bear & Company, 1990 ISBN 10: 1879181010, ISBN 13: 9781879181014

EMFs

Dr Samuel Milham *Dirty Electricity: Electrification and the diseases of civilization* iUniverse 2012 ISBN 10: 193890818X, ISBN-13: 978-1938908187

Dr Andrew Marino *Going Somewhere: A life of truth and science.* Cassandra, 2011. ISBN-13: 978-0981854915

Dr Martin Blank *Overpowered: what science tells us about the dangers of cell phones and other wifi-age devices,* Seven Stories Press 2014 ISBN-10: 1609805097, ISBN 13: 978-1609805098

Dr George Carlo Cell Phones: invisible hazards in the wireless age: an insider's alarming discoveries about cancer and genetic damage, Basic Books 2002 ISBN 10: 078670960X,
ISBN 13: 978-0786709601

Electrohypersensitivity (EHS)

https://www.emfanalysis.com
http://www.electricsense.com/
http://www.clearlightventures.com/
http://www.weepinitiative.org/

Mitigation

http://www.powerwatch.org.uk/
http://www.emfwise.com/
http://www.emraustralia.com.au/
http://www.emfsafe.com.au/

Research/Advocacy

https://www.emf-portal.org/en
http://www.bioinitiative.org/
http://www.radiationresearch.org
http://www.iemfa.org
http://microwavenews.com
http://www.magdahavas.com
http://andrewamarino.com
http://ehtrust.org
http://www.parentsforsafetechnology.org
http://safertechsolutions.org
http://emrpolicy.org
http://www.emfresearch.com/

About the author

Jason Bawden-Smith is an Australian born and educated environmental scientist with extensive knowledge and experience of the impact of chemicals and pathogens on human health and the broader environment. Jason has over twenty-five years diversified environmental health experience, ranging from environmental risk communication and management to health risk assessments for metals, persistent organic chemicals, and other hazardous materials. In recent years Jason has been researching, investigating and developing cost-effective solutions to the adverse impact of EMFs on human health and the environment.

Jason holds a both a Bachelor of Applied Science in Environmental Health and a Master's degree in Environmental Science. During his short career in academia, he published eleven peer-reviewed papers, including three in the prestigious *Medical Journal of Australia*, and he has presented at numerous national and international environmental conferences.

Jason Bawden-Smith is also a successful entrepreneur, author and speaker. He has founded four companies during his business career, including one of largest and most successful contaminated land consultancy companies in Australia (100 employees and a revenue of $30 million). His current project, EMF Warriors, has an ambitious goal to educate one billion people on the health benefits of reconnecting with nature and the importance of minimising exposure to technology.

Publications

Bawden-Smith J. Reducing Contaminated Soil Rehabilitation Costs – Review of Portable XRF Performance

On Australian Soils. Journal of the Australian Institute Of Mining and Metallurgy 6:17-19, 2001

Bawden-Smith J. *Managing Metal Contaminated Soils.* What's New in Waste Management 62:44-46, 2000

Davis, J., Bawden-Smith, J. *2000. Management of lead contaminated soil from 67 Residential Properties using field portable X-Ray Fluorescence.* Proceedings of the Australian and New Zealand Institute of Waste Management Annual Conference, 2000

Ridings M, Shorter AJ, Bawden-Smith J. *Strategies for the Investigation of Contaminated Sites Using Field Potable X-Ray Fluorescence Techniques.* Commun. Soil Sci. Plant Anal, 31:11-14, 2000

Lemmon JM, McAnulty JM, Bawden-Smith J. *Outbreak of cryptosporidiosis linked to an indoor swimming pool.* Med J. Aust 1996; 165: 613-616

Mira M, Bawden-Smith J, Causer J, Alperstein A, Karr M, Snitch P, Waller G, Fett J. *Blood lead concentrations of pre-school children in Central and Southern Sydney.* Med J. Aust 164:399-402, 1996

Gulson BL, Davis J, Mizon KJ, Korsch MJ, Bawden-Smith J. *Sources of lead in soil and dust and the use of dust fallout as a sampling medium.* Sci Total Environ 166:245-262, 1995

Gulson B, Davis J, Bawden-Smith J. *Paint as a source of re-contamination of houses in urban environments and its role in maintaining elevated blood lead levels in children.* Sci Total Environ; 164:221-235, 1995

Fett MJ, Mira M, Bawden-Smith J, Alperstein G, Causer J, Karr M, Gulson B, Cannata S. *Children's blood lead levels and environmental lead contamination.* (letter) Med J. Aust; 158: 506, 1993

Fett MJ, Mira M, Bawden-Smith J, Causer J, Brokenshire T, Gulson B, Alperstein G. *Community prevalence survey of childhood blood lead levels and environmental lead contamination in inner Sydney.* Med J Aust 157; 441-5, 1992

Bawden-Smith J, Mira M, Fett MJ, Alperstein G, Gulson B, Brokenshire T, Cannata S. *Mort Bay, Balmain pilot study of blood lead in children. Public Health Unit for central and Southern Sydney,* September 1992

About EMF Warriors

EMF Warriors is a global movement of concerned citizens who realise modern electronic devices produce electromagnetic fields (EMF) that are not native to this earth (nnEMFs). These nnEMFs are completely foreign to human biology and are wreaking havoc on the health and wellbeing of our families and our planet. The body of scientific evidence linking nnEMF to many adverse health conditions and diseases is compelling. New quantum biology research suggests that nnEMF is the underlying cause of almost all modern diseases.

We appreciate and are grateful for the benefits technology provides to society. We are not anti-technology, rather advocates for safe technology. We are confident that once governments and industry acknowledge that our modern indoor lifestyle and electronic devices are harming us, our brilliant scientists and engineers will collaborate to develop a win–win solution so we can continue to enjoy using our technology safely.

Identifying and mitigating sources of nnEMF is critically important and we will provide you with simple ways to test your home and provide sound, science-based advice and recommend practical solutions to reduce your exposure. But just as important is arming you with the knowledge and evidence that reconnecting to the healing EMFs provided by nature can reverse the negative impact of nnEMF. This is a balanced approach or what we call good personal EMF hygiene.

The founders and associated experts are constantly searching journals, conferences and the internet for the latest research and cutting edge information and knowledge on everything to do with EMFs. Once we have vetted the information we add the video, audio or paper to our library – think "Spotify for EMF knowledge". Our library is the best free one-stop-shop for EMF knowledge on the planet, it's a lighthouse for those lost in a sea of invisible EMF. We help explain complex issues in simple, easy-to-understand formats while also allowing professionals to dive deep into big topics like quantum biology and electrical engineering. However, our efforts don't end there. We provide, promote and support awareness campaigns, conduct interviews and lecture on all things EMF.

EMF Warriors is here for you. We want to provide information, resources and solutions to your most pressing nnEMF concerns and needs. We will be holding regular Q&A sessions, interviewing experts and continually adding the best content to our library. It's easy to blame others for the state of the world we find ourselves in. But we all have to take responsibility as we have embraced the technology with open arms, even lined up in long queues outside stores to have in our hands the latest wireless technology. Personal EMF hygiene starts at home where you and your children spend most of your time. One person, one home, one community at a time.

Visit **www.emfwarriors.com** now and get immediate free access to everything you need. The future of our children's health depends on you taking action.

Index

Lightning Source UK Ltd.
Milton Keynes UK
UKOW01f0117100917
308850UK00001B/17/P